Thermal properties

Advanced Physics Project for Independent Learning

Student's Guide

John Murray
in association with
Inner London Education Authority

Introduction to the Unit

This is one of the four second level APPIL Units and it is a study of heat and some of the thermal properties of liquids, solids and gases. Heat is defined as the energy which is transferred from a body at a high temperature to one at a lower temperature. The Unit therefore begins with a study of the subtle idea of temperature and its measurement. Chapter 2 discusses how temperature changes and change of phase are used to measure the amount of energy transferred by heating. The concept of an ideal gas temperature scale is introduced in chapter 1 and a molecular model of an ideal gas is developed in chapter 3 to predict the behaviour of gases. Chapter 4 discusses how the predictions of this model are related to the behaviour of real gases and vapours. In chapters 5 and 6 a study is made of two important heating processes, the transfer of energy by conduction and by radiation.

This Unit develops the ideas introduced in the Unit *Structure of matter* on temperature, the gas laws, and the kinetic theory model of matter.

Organising your study

The aims and objectives of each chapter are particularly important in organising your learning because they tell you what you should be able to do at the end of each chapter. Use these objectives in making any summary notes you think you require to supplement answers to study questions and other questions.

Try to answer the questions on objectives at the end of each chapter without referring to the Unit or your reference texts, so that the questions will provide a way of assessing whether you have achieved the required objectives.

Activities

Remember this is a course in which you learn through a variety of activities. You learn by:

reading the Unit text and reference books;

answering questions, which may involve you in the development of an idea, test the understanding and application of your knowledge, or guide your use of books and other resources;

doing the experiments, instructions for which are provided at the back of this book;

using the audio-visual material and the computer program included in this Unit.

Organising your time

Use the information at the opening of each chapter to organise laboratory work in the best sequence. The *progress monitor* will help you to plan your work so that you complete it in the recommended study time, which assumes that you spend 8 to 10 hours each week on physics.

You should spend 7 to 8 weeks on this Unit, divided as follows:

Chapter 1	½ week	Chapter 4	1 week
Chapter 2	1½ weeks	Chapter 5	1½ weeks
Chapter 3	2 weeks	Chapter 6	1 week

Contents

Chapter 1

Temperature and its measurement

Aim

In this chapter you will review the concept of temperature, and how a scale of temperature may be defined. The principles involved in developing a thermodynamic scale of temperature will be studied, and various methods of temperature measurement will be discussed.

Objectives

When you have completed the work in this chapter you should be able to:

1 Use the following scientific terms correctly:
thermal equilibrium, thermal contact, thermometric property, thermocouple, thermoelectric e.m.f.

2 Define the following terms:
ice point, steam point, triple point, absolute zero, ideal gas temperature, kelvin, Celsius thermodynamic temperature.

3 Explain what is meant by a temperature scale, and state how such a scale can be established in terms of a varying physical property using
(a) the triple point of water,
(b) two fixed points (e.g. the ice point and the steam point).

4 Describe how a change in temperature affects:
(a) the volumes of liquids and solids,
(b) the pressure and volume of a fixed mass of gas,
(c) the electrical resistance of metallic conductors and semiconductors,
(d) the thermoelectric e.m.f. of a thermocouple.

5 Describe the principles of construction, the method of calibration, the uses and the limitations of:
(a) liquid-in-glass thermometers,
(b) gas thermometers,
(c) electrical resistance thermometers,
(d) thermoelectric thermometers.

6 Explain the term International Practical Temperature Scale and state the reasons for adopting this scale.

7 EXTENSION
Define expansivity, and explain the thermal expansion of solids in terms of the molecular theory of matter.

Experiments in chapter 1
There are no experiments in this chapter.

References
Adkins   Chapter 1
Duncan MM   Chapter 4
Hands   Chapter 2
Millar   Chapter 10
Nelkon   Chapters 8 and 16
Whelan   Chapters 21 and 22

Study time: ½ week

1.1 Temperature

Our first appreciation of the idea of temperature is linked with sensations of hotness and coldness, experienced through touch. An object feels cool to our touch if heat flows from our body to the object when we hold it. We can develop a more exact concept of temperature by considering what happens when two systems or bodies are placed in thermal contact. The systems in thermal contact will change in some way as their internal energy is redistributed. If these changes cease, we say that *thermal equilibrium* is established. When the two systems are first brought into thermal contact, they may or may not be in thermal equilibrium. What property of these two systems determines whether or not there is thermal equilibrium? Mass, density, charge, magnetic state, etc., are *not* the determining factors. We conclude that there is a property of a system called *temperature* which determines whether or not one system is in thermal equilibrium with another.

Q **1.1 Self-assessment question**
(a) State the zeroth law of thermodynamics and use it to explain the idea of bodies being 'at the same temperature' (see section 2.3 of the Unit *Structure of matter*).
(b) Are you in thermal contact with the sun? Explain.
(c) Are you in thermal equilibrium with the atmosphere? How would you verify your answer?∎

The temperature is described by a number, the same number for all systems or bodies in thermal equilibrium with each other. An arbitrary scale of these numbers is chosen, so that when bodies are placed in thermal contact heat always flows from the body at higher temperature to that at lower temperature. Temperature is a *fundamental quantity* (like mass and length) which cannot be defined in terms of other quantities, and so the *unit* in which temperature is measured is an *arbitrary* choice (like the units kilogram and metre).

1.2 Scales of temperature

Consider now what is required to construct a thermometer and devise a scale of temperature which will describe degrees of hotness.

1   To construct a thermometer, we choose some property of a given substance which changes continuously with temperature – a *thermometric property*. Galileo's early thermometer used the volume of air trapped in a glass bulb as the property; you are more familiar with thermometers using the length of a mercury column in a glass capillary tube as the property.

2   A scale of temperature is defined by drawing a straight line graph to relate the variation in thermometric property X with temperature measured on this particular scale.

3   The unknown temperature can be measured on this particular scale by finding the value of X at the unknown temperature and using the graph to find the corresponding point on the temperature scale.

One way of obtaining the defining graph is to choose two fixed points (temperatures which can be precisely reproduced) and to find the values of the property X at these two points. Temperatures at which two or more phases of a substance are in equilibrium at a particular pressure provide good fixed points, for example: normal boiling points (equilibrium temperature between vapour and liquid under standard pressure); normal freezing points; sublimation points; triple points (equilibrium between solid, liquid and gas at a unique temperature and pressure).

The original centigrade (hundred step) scale devised by Celsius used the ice point and the steam point as the fixed points, and designated them as 0 °C and 100 °C. Figure 1.1 shows how such a practical centigrade scale can be established using property X. The value of an unkown temperature θ can be measured on this particular scale by measuring the value of the property at the unknown temperature, X_θ.

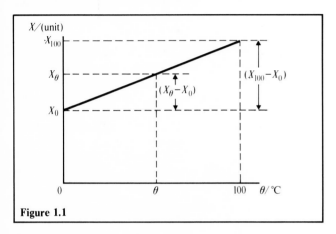

Figure 1.1

Q **1.2 Development question**
(a) From the graph (figure 1.1) write down expressions for the change in X per division (degree) (i) between 0 °C and θ, and (ii) between 0 °C and 100 °C.
(b) Hence show that

$$\frac{\theta}{100} = \frac{X_\theta - X_0}{X_{100} - X_0} \quad \blacksquare$$

Note: This equation is of practical as well as historical interest, since it defines one particular centigrade (now called Celsius) scale based on property X. It does *not*, however, define the Celsius thermodynamic scale (see section 1.3).

Another way of obtaining the defining graph uses one fixed point only, as illustrated in figure 1.2. In 1954, the triple point of water was chosen as the one defining fixed point in modern thermometry and was given the arbitrary temperature 273.16 K, for reasons which will be explained later (K is the symbol for the kelvin – the SI unit of temperature).

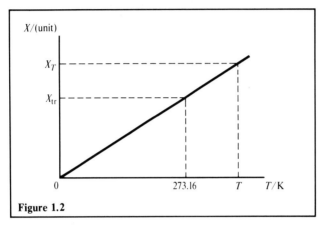

Figure 1.2

Using this fixed point, we define a temperature T on a scale based on property X by the equation

$$\frac{T}{273.16} = \frac{X_T}{X_{tr}}$$

where X_T and X_{tr} are the values of property X at temperature T and at the triple point respectively. Figure 1.3 shows a triple point cell used for calibrating a thermometer.

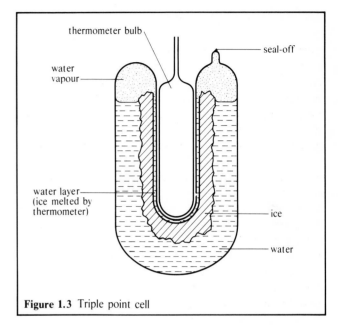

Figure 1.3 Triple point cell

Q **1.3 Self-assessment question**
(a) What is meant by the triple point of water?
(b) The resistance of the coil of a resistance thermometer is 6.73 Ω when calibrated at the triple point of water. Its resistance becomes 8.67 Ω at the normal boiling point of a liquid. What is this temperature on the resistance thermometer scale? ■

Disagreement between thermometers

It is important to realise that each physical property of a particular substance can define a temperature scale. We often speak of Fahrenheit and Centigrade scales, but these names just describe different ways of calibrating the thermometer. What does a scientist mean by a scale of temperature? It is a scale fixed by a particular kind of thermometer and defined by the chosen fixed points and the physical properties of a particular substance. Examples of such scales are the platinum resistance scale, the hydrogen constant volume scale and the mercury-in-glass scale. The temperature recorded will depend upon the type of thermometer being used. Figure 1.4 shows the temperature differences, $\Delta\theta$, between the temperatures recorded on a centigrade mercury-in-glass scale θ_{Hg}, and the temperatures recorded on two other scales.

Q **1.4 Self-assessment question**
(a) Explain why the temperature obtained for the boiling point of alcohol depends on the type of thermometer that is used.
(b) Use the data in figure 1.4 to obtain a graph of temperature difference $\Delta\theta$ between the thermocouple scale and the platinum resistance scale (y-axis) against temperature on the platinum resistance scale θ_R (x-axis). Estimate the values of temperatures on the thermocouple scale for temperatures of 25 °C, 50 °C and 75 °C on the platinum resistance scale.■

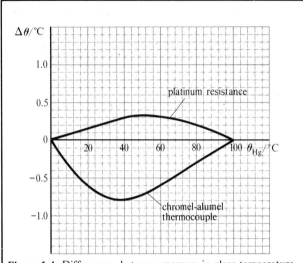

Figure 1.4 Differences between mercury-in-glass temperature scale and two other scales

1.3 Thermodynamic temperature

The fact that a measured temperature is dependent upon the physical properties of a particular thermometer is very inconvenient. It raises the question of whether temperature can be defined in such a way that the numerical value of the measured temperature is independent of the way in which it is measured. We need a scale of temperature which does not depend upon the thermometric properties of a particular substance.

One such scale was developed by Lord Kelvin and is called the *thermodynamic* scale. It is based on the theoretical efficiency of a perfectly reversible heat engine (the detailed reasoning is beyond the requirements of this course). This scale has been made identical to the scale of temperature based on the behaviour of an ideal or perfect gas.

In the search for a scale of temperature which does not depend on a particular substance, it is significant to find that gas thermometers using a scale based on the variation of pressure of a constant volume of gas show very close agreement whether the gas is oxygen, hydrogen, helium or some other gas. At very low pressures the agreement is much closer, converging to perfect agreement at zero pressure.

Figure 1.5 shows the way in which the readings of several gas thermometers, recording the temperature of condensing steam, approach the same value of 373.15 K as the pressure is reduced to zero. In chapters 3 and 4 we shall study a model of an ideal gas (defined as one which satisfies the equation pV = constant at a particular temperature) and learn how the behaviour of real gases approaches the ideal gas model behaviour as the pressure is reduced (i.e. when the molecules are well separated).

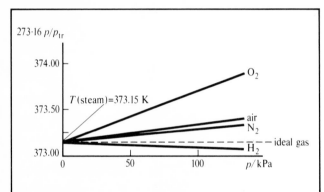

Figure 1.5 Readings of a constant volume gas thermometer for the temperature of condensing steam, when different gases are used at various values of p

We can define an *ideal gas temperature scale* using the pressure of a constant volume of ideal gas as the thermometric property and taking the standard fixed point, the triple point, as 273.16 K.

Q **1.5 Self-assessment question**
Write down the defining equation for the ideal gas temperature T.■

This ideal gas scale can be realised from the behaviour of real gases, by extrapolating the results to zero pressure. We can express temperature on the ideal gas scale as

$$T = 273.16 \lim_{p \to 0} \left(\frac{p_T}{p_{tr}} \right) \text{K}$$

where p_T and p_{tr} are the gas pressures at temperature T and the triple point respectively. Since variations of pressure or volume, or both, can be used to define a temperature scale, a more general equation is

$$T = 273.16 \lim_{p \to 0} \frac{(pV)_T}{(pV)_{tr}} \text{K}$$

The zero of the scale, 0 K or *absolute zero*, is the temperature at which the product, pV, is zero for an ideal gas. This is the temperature at which the energy of molecular motion becomes minimum; the thermal energy of the gas is zero and it possesses only *zero point energy* (see chapter 3).

Celsius temperature scale

The choice of the value 273.16 K for the thermodynamic temperature of the triple point of water is made so that, to the best available experimental results, there are exactly 100 K between the ice point and the steam point.

T_{tr} = 273.16 K (by definition)
T_{ice} = 273.15 K (by experimental determination)
T_{steam} = 373.15 K (by experimental determination)

The Celsius thermodynamic scale has its zero at the ice point and the unit on this scale is the degree Celsius (° C) which is an identical temperature interval to the kelvin (K).

Celsius thermodynamic temperature θ is defined by the equation

$$\theta/°C = T/K - 273.15$$

Note: Celsius temperatures are called *common temperatures* to distinguish them from kelvin thermodynamic temperatures. Common and thermodynamic temperatures differ only by a shift in the zero of 273.15 K. So Celsius is not just another name for any centigrade scale based on 100 divisions between the ice and steam points.

The degree Celsius is identical to the kelvin, and at the moment the best measurements give 100 K or 100 Celsius degrees between the ice and steam points. The symbol θ will be used for temperatures in degrees Celsius, but temperature intervals will be given in kelvins.

Q **1.6 Self-assessment question**
Define the kelvin. Is it true to say that the interval between the ice point and the steam point is by definition 100 K? Explain your answer.■

1.4 Properties which depend on temperature

Thermometers are based on the variation of a property with temperature, so before making any quantitative study of the variation of a particular property with temperature, it was necessary to clarify what we mean by temperature and know why we must specify the scale on which temperature is measured.

Q 1.7 Self-assessment question

(a) Your friend says that the volume of mercury must increase uniformly with temperature because mercury is a very good thermometric liquid. Comment on this statement.
(b) How would you test experimentally whether a particular physical property changes uniformly with temperature.■

Now consider briefly some properties of a substance which vary with temperature, and assess the suitability of these changing properties for measuring temperature.

Expansion

The volume of a solid, liquid or gas increases when the substance is heated. The *cubical expansivity* measures the fractional increase in volume per kelvin rise; it is of the order of 10^{-5} K^{-1} for solids, 10^{-3} K^{-1} for liquids. Although the fractional change in dimensions of solids is very small, the forces associated with expansion and contraction are very large, as is evident if we attempt to prevent the changes.

Q 1.8 Self-assessment question

How can the expansion of a solid be employed in measuring temperature?■

SYLLABUS EXTENSION

For solids, expansion can also be expressed in terms of increase in length and increase in area.

Q 1.9 Self-assessment question

(a) Write down a definition of linear expansivity α.
(b) Derive an equation for the length of a solid bar which has been heated to a temperature θ, if its length at 0 °C was l_0.
(c) Would you expect α to be constant (i) for all ranges of temperature and (ii) for all directions in a solid?■

Q 1.10 Self-assessment question

A steel bar, length 1.0 m and cross-sectional area 0.50 cm², is heated through 10 K. Calculate
(a) the increase in length of the steel bar if it is free to expand,
(b) the force which would be exerted by the rod if it was not allowed to expand.
(Linear expansivity of steel = 1.2×10^{-5} K^{-1}, the Young modulus of steel = 2.0×10^{11} Pa.)■

Q 1.11 Study question

Study and sketch a curve of the variation of intermolecular force with separation (such as figure 2.2 in the Unit *Structure of matter*), marking the equilibrium separation. Using this curve
(a) explain why an atom in a solid vibrates with greater amplitude on one side of the equilibrium position,
(b) describe how the mean position of the vibration changes as the amplitude increases, and
(c) explain why a solid expands when heated.■

Since the volume of a gas is dependent on the pressure, the cubic expansivity or volume coefficient of expansion of a gas, α, is defined for constant pressure conditions. α is the volume increase per kelvin measured as a fraction of the volume V_0 at the ice point. The expansion is $V_0\alpha$ for every kelvin rise, so the volume at θ, V_θ, is given by $V_\theta = V_0 (1 + \alpha\theta)$.

Q 1.12 Self-assessment question

(a) 'Scales of temperature based on the expansion of different gases at constant pressure are all in close agreement with each other and with the kelvin thermodynamic scale.' Explain how the value of cubic expansivity α for gases is related to this statement.
(b) If a constant volume hydrogen thermometer gives temperatures in very close agreement with the ideal gas scale, what can you say about the value of β, the pressure coefficient, if $p_\theta = p_0 (1 + \beta\theta)$? What scale are you assuming θ is measured on?■

Electrical resistance

Q 1.13 Self-assessment question

(a) Give a brief explanation of how the 'free electron' theory accounts for the increase in the resistance of a metallic conductor with temperature.
(b) Why does the electrical resistance of a semiconductor decrease as it is heated?■

Q 1.14 Self-assessment question

The resistance of a particular metallic conductor at a temperature θ, measured on the ideal gas Celsius scale, is given by the equation

$$R_\theta = R_0 \left(1 + \alpha\theta + \beta\theta^2\right)$$

where R_0 is the resistance at 0 °C, $\alpha = 4.0 \times 10^{-3} \text{ K}^{-1}$ and $\beta = -6.0 \times 10^{-7} \text{ K}^{-2}$.
(a) Write down the value of R_{100} in terms of R_0.
(b) Calculate the temperature θ_{Pt} on this resistance thermometer scale when $\theta = 60$ °C. ■

For metallic conductors, the magnitude of β is very much less than that of α, so their resistances vary almost linearly with temperature over a wide range. The value of α, the temperature coefficient of resistance, is important in determining how closely a particular resistance scale agrees with the ideal gas scale.

Q 1.15 Self-assessment question

Values of α for some common metals are:
$4.0 \times 10^{-3} \text{ K}^{-1}$ for aluminium; $3.8 \times 10^{-3} \text{ K}^{-1}$ for platinum; $6.5 \times 10^{-3} \text{ K}^{-1}$ for iron. State, with a reason, which metal resistance scale will be in closest agreement with the ideal gas scale. ■

Thermoelectric e.m.f.

Thermocouple thermometers make use of the e.m.f. developed in a circuit containing two junctions of dissimilar conductors when the junctions are at different temperatures. One junction is maintained at a fixed reference temperature. The relationship between e.m.f. E and temperature difference ΔT is

$$E = \alpha\left(\Delta T\right) + \beta(\Delta T)^2$$

Figure 1.6 shows a typical curve.

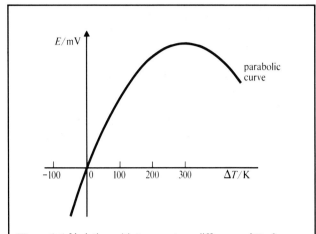

Figure 1.6 Variation with temperature difference ΔT of a typical thermoelectric e.m.f.

Q 1.16 Self-assessment question

(a) Is β a positive or a negative constant in this particular case?
(b) For what range of temperature difference would you use this thermocouple as a thermometer?
(c) Suggest suitable fixed reference temperatures for using this thermocouple to measure temperatures around (i) 350 K (ii) 750 K.
(d) What quantities would you measure to obtain an unknown temperature on the thermocouple scale? ■

Vapour pressure

In chapter 4 you will study how the pressure exerted by a saturated vapour increases with temperature. This is a property which forms the basis of some important thermometers.

Q 1.17 Self-assessment question

Listed below are the saturated vapour pressures p of water vapour at temperatures between 0 °C and 100 °C on the Celsius thermodynamic scale.

θ/°C	0	20	40	60	80	100
p/Pa	0.60	2.3	7.4	20	47	100

(a) Use the values of p_0 and p_{100} to calculate the temperature on the water vapour pressure scale when the Celsius temperature is 60 °C.
(b) Calculate the values of $\lg p$ and plot a graph of $\lg p$ against Celsius temperature.
(c) A thermometer scale can be constructed using $\lg p$ as the thermometric property X. Calculate the temperatures on a $\lg$ (water-vapour pressure) scale when the temperature is (i) 60 °C, and (ii) 84 °C. Comment on your answers in (a) and (c) and their relationship with the shape of the graph in (b). ■

Other properties which vary with temperature and are used as the basis for thermometers include:
the speed of sound in a gas;
the quality (colour) of electromagnetic radiation emitted by a hot source (optical pyrometers);
the quantity of electromagnetic radiation emitted by a hot source (total radiation pyrometers);
the magnetic susceptibility of a material.

1.5 Types of thermometer

What properties are needed to make a good thermometer? The following are some of the important criteria.

1 *Accuracy* – the ability to give an accurate value of thermodynamic temperature.

2 *Sensitivity* – the ability to respond to small changes of temperature.

3 *Consistency* – the readings must remain true over a long period of use without requiring recalibration (e.g. no zero drift).

4 *Suitability* – the thermometer may have to satisfy special requirements, such as: suitable range; robustness; portability; small size; rapid response; quickness of reading; low thermal capacity (so that it doesn't change the temperature it is recording).

It is obviously an advantage for a thermometer to have a wide range to make it a more versatile instrument, and in any particular range it is necessary to choose the best thermometer using the above criteria. Table 1.1 lists the ranges of some common thermometers.

Table 1.1

Type of thermometer	Range/K
mercury-in-glass	234 to 600
constant volume hydrogen	3 to 175
platinum resistance	83 to 1400
graphite resistance	above 3
thermocouple	25 to 1750
optical pyrometer	above 1250
total radiation pyrometer	above 500

Q 1.18 Study question

Make brief notes on the structures, and explain the principles of operation, of

(a) a constant volume gas thermometer,

(b) a thermoelectric thermometer, and

(c) an electrical resistance thermometer.■

Q 1.19 Self-assessment question

For each of the following purposes, choose the thermometer that you would use and explain why it is the best one for that purpose.

(a) Measuring the temperature in a steel furnace.

(b) Measuring the temperature of a patient in hospital.

(c) Calibrating other thermometers under laboratory conditions.

(d) Measuring very low temperatures.

(e) Measuring the temperature 200 m down an oil-well.■

International practical temperature scale

No thermometers exist which contain an ideal gas, and no two real thermometers are ever likely to agree except at the fixed points. It is only possible to say that a resistance thermometer measures temperature more accurately than a thermocouple thermometer if we are comparing how accurately they *each* record temperature on the ideal gas scale. We need to know how close to the perfect scale are the readings of a particular thermometer and then temperatures measured by a real thermometer can be corrected to what a non-existent ideal thermometer would read on the thermodynamic scale.

Compare figure 1.4 with figure 1.7. Figure 1.4 shows how a platinum resistance scale and a particular thermocouple scale differ from a mercury-in-glass scale. Having defined the thermodynamic scale we can show, as in figure 1.7, differences between readings on three thermometer scales and temperature on the Celsius thermodynamic scale.

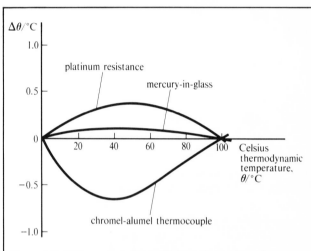

Figure 1.7 Differences between Celsius thermodynamic scale and some common thermometer scales

To reconcile results from different thermometers, and to obtain temperatures as close as possible to the ideal scale, a series of fixed points have been agreed internationally (e.g. the freezing points of gold and silver, the boiling point of oxygen). A particular thermometer is specified for measuring temperatures within a particular range and the temperature on the I.P.T.S. is calculated from an agreed equation.

In developing this international scale, the use of the hydrogen and helium gas thermometers has been very important, since these gases behave very nearly like an ideal gas.

Q 1.20 Study question*
(a) Explain what is meant by the International Practical Temperature Scale, and describe how it is defined.
(b) Why is this scale needed, and why is it described as a *practical* scale?
(c) What kind of thermometer is used for measuring temperatures on this scale between 200 K and 600 K and what information is required?∎

Questions on objectives

1 Explain how a scale of temperature is defined in terms of some suitable property of a particular material. Why do such scales generally not agree with each other?
(objectives 1, 3 and 6)

2 Which of the following statements is correct? Give a reason for your answer in each case.
(a) The temperature of the triple point of water is exactly 273.16 K.
(b) The temperature of the normal boiling point of water is exactly 100 °C.
(objective 2)

3 The graph in figure 1.8 shows the variation in resistance of a piece of platinum wire with the temperature being measured on the ideal gas scale. What is the *Celsius* temperature corresponding to a resistance of 17 Ω on
(a) the ideal gas scale, and
(b) the platinum resistance scale?
(objectives 2 and 3)

4 Discuss the relative merits of (i) a mercury-in-glass thermometer, (ii) a platinum resistance thermometer, (iii) a thermocouple for measuring the temperature of an oven which is maintained at approximately 550 K.
(objectives 4 and 5)

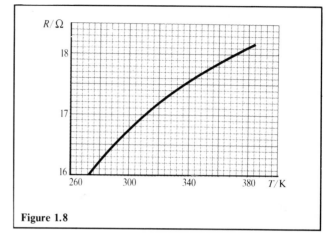

Figure 1.8

5 Explain the physical principles underlying one electrical method of measuring temperature that can be used in a school laboratory. Assuming that you possess a mercury thermometer correctly graduated in terms of the Celsius temperature scale, describe how you would calibrate the electrical thermometer for the temperature range 0-300 °C and how you would use it to measure temperature. How would you attempt to calibrate the electrical thermometer if no such mercury thermometer were available?

Discuss the advantages and disadvantages of the instrument you describe as a means of measuring temperature. Assuming that it is used for temperatures up to 600 °C, discuss the order of accuracy you would expect it to give at the higher temperatures outside its range of calibration.

(objective 5)

Chapter

2

Heat and its measurement

Aim

The aim of this chapter is to explain the terms specific heat capacity and specific latent heat and to develop an understanding of the principles of the measurement of heat transfers by measuring changes in temperature.

Objectives

When you have completed the work in this chapter you should be able to:

1 Use the following scientific terms correctly: calorimetry, change of phase, latent heat.

2 Define and use the following scientific terms: heat capacity, specific heat capacity, latent heat, specific latent heat of fusion, specific latent heat of vaporisation.

3 Recall the standard symbol and unit for each of the following terms: heat, heat capacity, specific heat capacity, latent heat, specific latent heat.

4 (a) Distinguish between heat, internal energy and temperature.
(b) State the relationship between heat transferred and observed change in temperature.

5 Perform and describe electrical methods to determine
(a) the specific heat capacity of a liquid,
(b) the specific latent heat of vaporisation.

6 Explain how the results of the experiments listed in objective 5 can be used to calculate the appropriate physical quantities.

7 Explain the principles of continuous flow calorimetry and describe how you would measure the specific heat capacity of a liquid by this method.

8 Solve problems involving: heat transferred to a body, specific heat capacities of liquids and solids, specific latent heat.

9 EXTENSION
Describe electrical methods to determine
(a) the specific heat capacity of a solid,
(b) the specific latent heat of fusion.

10 EXTENSION
Explain how the results of the experiments listed in objective 9 can be used to calculate the appropriate physical quantities.

11 EXTENSION
State Newton's law of cooling and explain a simple cooling correction.

Experiments in chapter 2

TP1 Specific heat capacity – electrical method (1 hour)
TP2 Specific heat capacity – continuous flow method (1 hour)
TP3 Specific latent heat of vaporisation (¾ hour)

References

Adkins   Chapter 2
Duncan MM   Chapter 4
Hands   Chapter 4
Millar   Chapter 9
Nelkon   Chapter 9
Whelan   Chapters 23 and 27

Chapter 2

Study time: 1½ weeks

2.1 The nature of heat

The first law of thermodynamics embodies the fundamental idea that energy is always conserved. The importance of the concept of energy derives from centuries of scientific thought and experiment, seeking to confirm that in an endless variety of interactions between bodies, in which so many properties and quantities change, something is conserved.

The conservation of energy implies that heat is a form of energy – a concept which only became accepted after centuries of debate, and after the experiments of men like Joule on increasing the internal energy of a body by providing energy in a variety of ways. Joule showed that heat corresponds in a precise way to work done (mechanically or electrically). Now the idea that heat is energy is a basic concept of physics; we measure heat in joules, and accept the kinetic theory of matter which relates rise in temperature to increase in the kinetic energy of particles of matter.

The *internal energy, U,* of a system may be stored as potential energy due to the arrangement of the molecules or as the kinetic energy (translational, rotational and vibrational) of the molecules.

Heat and *work* are terms used to describe energy in the process of transfer. The distinction between 'heat supplied' and 'work done' is only a distinction between the forms in which energy enters a system. We call the energy transfer 'work done' if it involves an ordered process like pushing a piston against a force. The energy transfer is called 'heat' if it takes place, by means of conduction, convection or radiation, because of a temperature difference between bodies and if it involves energy in a disordered form (i.e. random molecular motion).

When heat Q is supplied to a system, it may result in an increase in internal energy ΔU and may also provide energy to do external work W. Figure 2.1 is a representation of the first law of thermodynamics pictured as a balancing equation for this case. The block represents a total amount of energy which remains constant but is redistributed during the change.

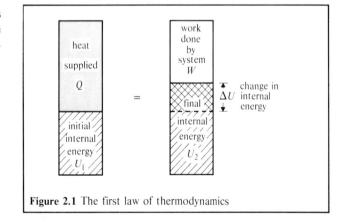

Figure 2.1 The first law of thermodynamics

The law can be summarised in symbols by the equation

➡ $$Q = W + \Delta U$$

In this case, we have taken Q as positive if heat is *supplied* to the system and W as positive if work is done *by* the system (e.g. by a gas in expanding).

Q 2.1 Self-assessment question

Write a sentence giving the meaning of each of the following terms: heat, energy and internal energy. ∎

The temperature of a body may rise because some work is done *on* the body. For example, a liquid can be heated by an electric immersion heater. Work done by the power supply in providing a current produces an increase in the internal energy of the conductor and of any other system (the liquid) which is in thermal contact with it.

In this chapter we shall be measuring the temperature changes and phase changes which occur when all the heat supplied produces an increase in internal energy and no external work is done. In this case $W = 0$, so $Q = \Delta U$.

2.2 Specific heat capacity

How do we measure the quantity of heat taken in by a substance? Consider first a transfer of heat which produces no change in phase. The increase in internal energy is indicated by a rise in temperature. This rise in temperature will depend upon the number of molecules in the substance and hence its mass. It will also depend upon the material itself, since different substances of the same mass differ in the quantity of heat required to cause the same increase in temperature. The quantity which enables comparisons to be made is called the *specific heat capacity*.

Suppose a quantity of heat Q is transferred to a substance of mass m and causes a change in temperature $\Delta\theta$, then the specific heat capacity c is defined by the equation

$$\blacktriangleright \quad c = \frac{Q}{m\,\Delta\theta}$$

In the expression for c, as $\Delta\theta$ tends to zero c approaches the specific heat capacity at a particular temperature. If $\Delta\theta$ is equal to $(\theta_2 - \theta_1)$, we measure the average value over that range. That is, we measure the average c between the temperatures θ_1 and θ_2 at a temperature of $(\theta_1 + \theta_2)/2$.

Q 2.2 Study question
(a) Write down a definition of specific heat capacity in words.
(b) What is the unit of specific heat capacity?
(c) Write down an equation which will enable you to find the energy Q which must be supplied to a body to produce a rise in temperature $\Delta\theta$ (or must be removed to produce a fall in temperature of $\Delta\theta$).

(d) Explain what is meant by the heat capacity or thermal capacity of a body.
(e) What is the unit of heat capacity?∎

Q 2.3 Self-assessment question
(a) What is the unit of heat?
(b) If the temperature of a 2.0 kg mass of copper increases by 30 K, what is the energy supplied? (The specific heat capacity of copper is 4.0×10^2 J kg^{-1} K^{-1}.)
(c) A steel hammer of mass 0.50 kg hits the 2.0 kg piece of copper and, as a result, the temperature rises 0.050 °C, what was the speed of the hammer just before impact (assuming 75% of the hammer's kinetic energy was transformed into internal energy in the copper)?∎

Q 2.4 Self-assessment question
(a) Why does water from a hot tap normally run cold for a few seconds after the tap has been turned on?
(b) How much heat is transferred from hot water at 55 °C in heating a copper pipe from room temperature, 15 °C, to 55 °C? The pipe is 4.0 m long and the cross-sectional area of the copper in the pipe is 3.0×10^{-4} m^2.
(Specific heat capacity of copper = 4.0×10^2 J kg^{-1} K^{-1}, density of copper = 9.0×10^3 kg m^{-3}.)∎

Q 2.5 Self-assessment question
(a) What is the current drawn by a 240 V immersion heater in a hot water tank of mass 2.0 kg in a house if it is to increase the temperature of 20 kg of water from 15 °C to 75 °C in 30 minutes? Assume that the tank is well lagged and made from copper.
(Specific heat capacity of copper = 4.0×10^2 J kg^{-1} K^{-1}, specific heat capacity of water = 4.2×10^3 J kg^{-1} K^{-1}.)
(b) Estimate the cost of heating water for a bath.∎

Variation of specific heat capacity

Q 2.6 Self-assessment question
Figure 2.2 is a graph of the specific heat capacity of copper as a function of temperature. What does this graph show about the way in which the specific heat capacity of copper varies with temperature?∎

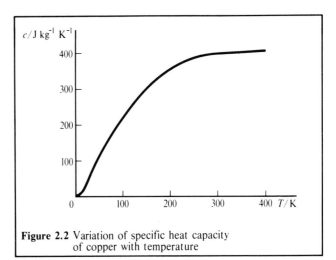

Figure 2.2 Variation of specific heat capacity of copper with temperature

The value of c also depends upon whether it is measured at constant pressure (c_p) or at constant volume (c_V).

Q 2.7 Self-assessment question
Why do you think that for solids and liquids it is always c_p that is measured?∎

Molar heat capacity

Sometimes the heat capacity is referred to one mole of material instead of unit mass (the concept of the mole is revised in Appendix 1). The molar heat capacity is an important quantity when different elements are compared.

Q 2.8 Self-assessment question

Table 2.1 lists the molar masses and specific heat capacities (at 0 °C) of a number of elements. Calculate the molar heat capacities of each of the listed elements. Comment on the results.■

Table 2.1

Element	M_m/kg mol^{-1}	c_p/J K^{-1} kg^{-1}
aluminium	0.0270	877
copper	0.0635	380
lead	0.2072	126
sodium	0.0230	1184

2.3 Measurement of specific heat capacity

Obtaining accurate values of specific heat capacity provides scientists with important information for predicting the behaviour of materials, and much thought has gone into devising experiments for this measurement. To measure how much heat has been transferred to a substance, it is necessary to eliminate heat transfer to other bodies and the surroundings, or to find ways of calculating these heat losses. Both these methods are difficult in practice, so measuring heat transfer tends to be one of the less accurate measurements in physics.

Electrical methods

Electrical heating is one of the most convenient ways of transferring energy, and modern methods of measuring specific heat capacities use this.

For liquids, a heating coil can be immersed in a liquid of mass m in a calorimeter of heat capacity C. The initial temperature of the liquid θ_1 is recorded. A steady current I is passed through the coil and the p.d. across it is V. After a time t the current is switched off and the final temperature of the liquid is θ_2. Assuming that no energy loss occurs, we have

$$\begin{array}{ccc} \text{energy transferred} & = \text{energy gained} & + \text{energy gained} \\ \text{by heater} & \text{by liquid} & \text{by calorimeter} \end{array}$$

$$IVt = mc(\theta_2 - \theta_1) + C(\theta_2 - \theta_1)$$

where c is the specific heat capacity of the liquid and C is the heat capacity of the calorimeter.

E Experiment TP1
Specific heat capacity – electrical method

In this experiment you will determine the specific heat capacity of a liquid and estimate the errors involved in the measurements.

Q 2.9 Self-assessment question

Figure 2.3 shows a simple form of laboratory apparatus which is suitable for measuring the specific heat capacities of solids which are good conductors of heat. An aluminium cylinder of mass 2.0 kg has a 60 W electric heater fitted into one hole and a thermometer in a second hole. During an experiment to find the specific heat capacity of aluminium, the room temperature was 10.0 °C and the electric heater was switched off after a time of 500 s. The following readings of temperature θ and time t were obtained.

θ/°C	10.0	10.5	11.7	14.3	16.8	19.4	21.9	22.5	22.2
t/s	0	50	100	200	300	400	500	600	700

(a) Plot a graph of the results and calculate the specific heat capacity of the aluminium.
(b) What effect might changing the room temperature have on your result?
(c) Explain the curved section at each end of the graph.
(d) Is your result for the specific heat capacity higher or lower than it should be?
(e) Outline the additional precautions you would take to get a more accurate answer, and sketch on your graph the curve you would now expect to get.■

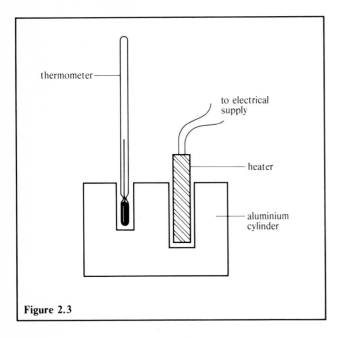

thermometer

to electrical supply

heater

aluminium cylinder

Figure 2.3

SYLLABUS EXTENSION

Q 2.10 Study question
Make brief notes on Nernst's method for finding the specific heat capacities of solids that are good conductors of heat. Give a labelled diagram of the apparatus, and show how a value for the specific heat capacity can be deduced from the experimental data.■

Continuous flow calorimetry

A method that can be used to measure the specific heat capacity of a liquid is a continuous flow method. In this type of experiment, heat losses are controlled and so can be allowed for. Callendar and Barnes devised a method which was used to investigate the variation of the specific heat capacity of water with temperature, in which water from a constant-head device flows through a glass tube and is heated by a heating coil. The electrical energy converted to internal energy in the resistor is given by

$$W = IVt$$

where V is the p.d. across the resistor, I is the current through it and t is the time. The heat transferred is

$$mc\,(\theta_2 - \theta_1) + Q$$

where m is the mass of water flowing in a time t and θ_2 and θ_1 are the outlet and inlet temperatures respectively. Q is the energy lost to the surroundings in time t. Then

$$IVt = mc\,(\theta_2 - \theta_1) + Q$$

where c is the specific heat capacity of the water.

E Experiment TP2
Specific heat capacity – continuous flow method
In this experiment you will determine the specific heat capacity of water by a continuous flow method.

Q 2.11 Study question
What are the advantages of continuous flow calorimetry?■

Q 2.12 Self-assessment question
In a continuous flow experiment the results in table 2.2 were obtained. Calculate the specific heat capacity of the liquid.■

Table 2.2

	Experiment 1	Experiment 2
current through the heating coil	3.0 A	2.5 A
potential difference across the heating coil	12 V	10 V
mass of liquid collected	420 g	650 g
time of experiment	60 s	120 s
inlet temperature	36 °C	36 °C
outlet temperature	40 °C	40 °C

2.4 Heat loss and cooling laws

Q 2.13 Study question
Give a brief outline of the precautions that must be taken in calorimetry experiments to minimise heat losses.■

Cooling correction

When heat is lost to the surroundings during a heat transfer experiment, a correction can be made to the observed maximum temperature which will give the estimated maximum temperature had no heat been lost. In applying a cooling correction, we usually assume that the rate of loss of heat is directly proportional to the temperature difference between the calorimeter and its surroundings. This is true for heat loss by conduction and by forced convection (e.g. a draught), also for heat loss by natural convection and radiation if the temperature difference is small.

To apply a simple cooling correction, record the temperature θ throughout the experiment and plot a graph of temperature against time, as illustrated in figure 2.4.

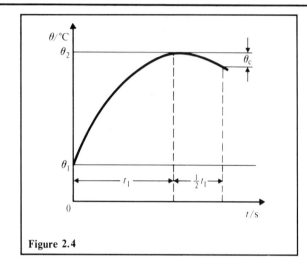

Figure 2.4

Q 2.14 Self-assessment question
Explain why the fall in temperature θ_c during half the time which is required to reach the maximum temperature θ_2 is the correction to be added to θ_2.■

Cooling laws

Q 2.15 Study question
(a) State Newton's law of cooling and the conditions under which it applies.
(b) What is the relationship between rate of loss of heat and excess temperature for cooling by natural convection? When does this law approximate to a linear relationship?■

Q 2.16 Self-assessment question
In an experiment to investigate a cooling law, a calorimeter containing oil was electrically heated, keeping the current and p.d. constant, until a steady temperature was attained. The temperature of the room was 20.0 °C. The current and p.d. were then increased in stages, and the new steady temperature noted each time. The series of results shown in table 2.3 was obtained.
(a) Why was the temperature steady despite the fact that energy was still being supplied?
(b) Plot a graph of the rate of loss of energy against excess temperature. Comment on your results.■

Table 2.3

Current I/A	Potential difference V/V	Steady temperature $\theta/°C$
0.8	4.8	41.0
1.0	6.2	50.0
1.2	7.8	62.0
1.6	11.9	94.0
2.0	16.8	137.0

The rate of loss of heat from a body is determined not only by the excess temperature, but also by the surface area, and the nature of the surface. For a body which has a uniform temperature θ and surface area A, if Newton's law of cooling applies,

$$\text{rate of loss of heat} = kA\,(\theta - \theta_0)$$

where θ_0 is the temperature of the surroundings and k is a constant depending upon the nature of the surface.

Q 2.17 Self-assessment question
Show that the rate of fall of temperature of a body is inversely proportional to a linear dimension. Hence explain why a small body cools faster than a large one.∎

2.5 Change of phase

Energy is needed to convert a solid to a liquid and a liquid to a vapour. The energy required to change the *phase* of a substance without changing its temperature is called the latent (hidden) heat L.

Note: The term phase relates to the fact that a substance can exist as a solid, a liquid or a gas. The chemical substance H_2O exists in the *solid phase* as ice, in the *liquid phase* as water and in the *gaseous phase* as steam. In your earlier work you may have used the term 'change of state' to describe the change from a solid to a liquid, but this phrase is now used in a more general way (see chapter 3, section 3.5).

Q 2.18 Self-assessment question
A solid (for example, naphthalene) was heated in a boiling tube by means of a heating coil and the temperature was recorded at half-minute intervals. The results were plotted on a graph, as shown in figure 2.5.
(a) What happened to the substance over the regions (i) A to B, (ii) B to C, (iii) C to D, (iv) D to E?
(b) Account for the fact that the temperature remained constant over the regions B to C and D to E, even though energy was still being transferred to the substance by the heating coil.∎

Q 2.19 Study question
(a) Define specific latent heat of fusion and specific latent heat of vaporisation.
(b) What is the unit of specific latent heat?
(c) Write an equation relating the energy Q required to change the phase of a substance without a change in temperature, to the mass m of the substance.∎

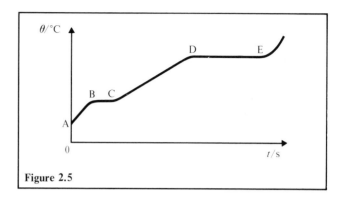

Figure 2.5

Q 2.20 Self-assessment question
(a) How much heat is required to change 5.0 kg of ice at 0 °C into water at 0 °C?
(b) If the same quantity of heat is now supplied to the water, what will be the water's final temperature?
(Specific latent heat of fusion of ice is 3.3×10^5 J kg^{-1}, specific heat capacity of water is 4.2×10^3 J kg^{-1} K^{-1}.)∎

Q 2.21 Self-assessment question
(a) Why is water used to cool car engines, despite the fact that it tends to produce corrosion? Some engines are air-cooled. What problems must be overcome?
(b) Calculate the heat required to change 5.0 kg of water which is initially at 20 °C into steam at 100 °C.
(The specific latent heat of vaporisation of water is 2.3×10^6 J kg^{-1}.)∎

Measurement of specific latent heat of vaporisation

An electrical method for the specific latent heat of vaporisation is illustrated in figure 2.6. The liquid is electrically heated by a heating coil. If I is the steady current through the coil and V the p.d. across it, the electrical energy supplied in a time t is IVt. When a steady state is reached, the rate at which the liquid is evaporating is equal to the rate at which it is condensing. If m is the mass of liquid which is collected in a time t, then

$$IVt = ml + Q$$

where l is the specific latent heat of the liquid and Q is the energy loss through the jacket in time t.

Q **2.22 Self-assessment question**
In an experiment to determine the specific latent heat of vaporisation of a volatile liquid by the method shown in figure 2.6, the results in table 2.4 were obtained. Determine the specific latent heat of vaporisation of the liquid and the rate of loss of energy from the calorimeter.■

Table 2.4

	Experiment 1	Experiment 2
current through the heating coil	3.0 A	4.0 A
p.d. across the heating coil	10.0 V	12.5 V
mass of liquid vaporised in 200 s	7.0 g	12.0 g

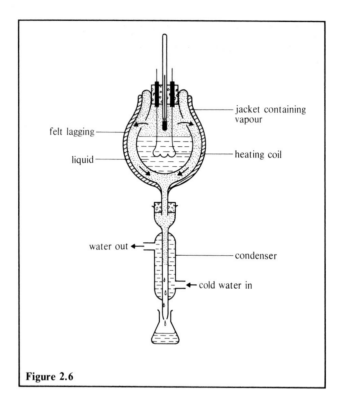

felt lagging

liquid

jacket containing vapour

heating coil

water out ◄

condenser

◄ cold water in

Figure 2.6

E **Experiment TP3**
Specific latent heat of vaporisation
The aim of this experiment is to determine a value for the specific latent heat of vaporisation of water by an electrical method (involving continuous flow).

SYLLABUS EXTENSION

Q **2.23 Study question**
Describe and explain an electrical method to measure the specific latent heat of fusion of a substance. You should give an outline of the experimental procedure, state what readings you would take, explain how you would use them to obtain a value and indicate how a correction for heat losses may be made.■

Q **2.24 Self-assessment question**
0.005 kg of water, initially at 20 °C, is poured into a large Dewar vessel containing liquid nitrogen at its boiling point (-196 °C). Calculate the mass of nitrogen vaporised.
(Specific latent heat of fusion of ice $= 3.3 \times 10^5$ J kg^{-1}, specific heat capacity of water $= 4.2 \times 10^3$ J kg^{-1} K^{-1}, mean specific heat capacity of ice $= 2.2 \times 10^3$ J kg^{-1} K^{-1}, specific latent heat of vaporisation of nitrogen $= 2.5 \times 10^5$ J kg^{-1}.)■

Q 2.25 Self-assessment question

A solar furnace has a large concave reflector which concentrates energy onto the surface of a boiler to heat water. Several types of reflector and boiler are available to make up the furnace and data for these are given in table 2.5. All the reflectors have an efficiency of 95%. Water enters the boiler at a temperature of 27 °C and steam is produced at a temperature of 100 °C. Using the information given, calculate which combinations of reflector and boiler will produce steam at the rate of at least 0.04 kg s^{-1}. Which of these combinations is cheapest?

Intensity of solar radiation (energy falling on 1 m^2 in 1 s) = 1.35×10^3 W m^{-2},
specific heat capacity of water = 4.2×10^3 J kg^{-1} K^{-1},
specific latent heat of steam = 2.3×10^6 J kg^{-1}. ■

Table 2.5

Reflectors			Boilers		
type	surface area	cost	type	energy loss	cost
A	20 m²	£100	E	30%	£300
B	60 m²	£300	F	25%	£450
C	100 m²	£500	G	20%	£600
D	120 m²	£800	H	15%	£750

Questions on objectives

1 Distinguish between specific heat capacity and specific latent heat. With what physical change is each associated?

(objective 2)

2 The following (**A–E**) are units of five physical quantities.

A K
B J
C J kg^{-1} K^{-1}
D J K^{-1}
E J kg^{-1}

Which of these is an acceptable unit of the following quantities?
(a) specific latent heat
(b) absolute temperature
(c) specific heat capacity
(d) heat capacity

(objective 3)

3 Explain the difference between the terms heat, internal energy and temperature.

(objective 4)

4 Draw a labelled diagram of the apparatus to measure the specific heat capacity of a liquid by the continuous flow method. List the measurements that you would take and indicate how you would calculate the specific heat capacity of the liquid. State two advantages of this method.

(objective 7)

5 Outline briefly an electrical method of measuring the specific latent heat of vaporisation of a liquid. Show how you would derive the specific latent heat from your measurements.

(objectives 5 and 6)

6 A lead pellet is fired at a sheet of steel and, on striking, the pellet melts. If the temperature of the pellet just before striking is 15 °C and lead melts at 327 °C, calculate the minimum speed of the pellet if only 15% of its energy is absorbed by the steel plate.
(Specific heat capacity and specific latent heat of fusion of lead are 1.3×10^2 J kg^{-1} K^{-1} and 2.1×10^4 J kg^{-1} respectively.)

(objective 8)

7 When a piece of ice of mass 6.00×10^{-4} kg at a temperature of -1 °C is dropped into liquid nitrogen boiling at -196 °C in a vacuum flask, 8.00×10^{-4} m^3 of nitrogen, measured at 21 °C and a pressure of 1.01×10^5 Pa, are produced. Calculate the mean specific heat capacity of ice.
(The specific latent heat of vaporisation of nitrogen is 2.13×10^5 J kg^{-1}, the density of nitrogen at s.t.p. is 1.25 kg m^{-3}.)
Hint: Determine the volume of nitrogen at s.t.p. using the relationship

$$\frac{p_1 V_1}{T_1} = \frac{p_2 V_2}{T_2}$$

(objective 8)

8 EXTENSION
State Newton's law of cooling and outline a simple cooling correction.

(objective 11)

Chapter 3

Aim

The aim of this chapter is to develop a model – the kinetic theory model of an ideal gas – and to discover to what extent the properties of gases can be predicted and explained on the basis of this model.

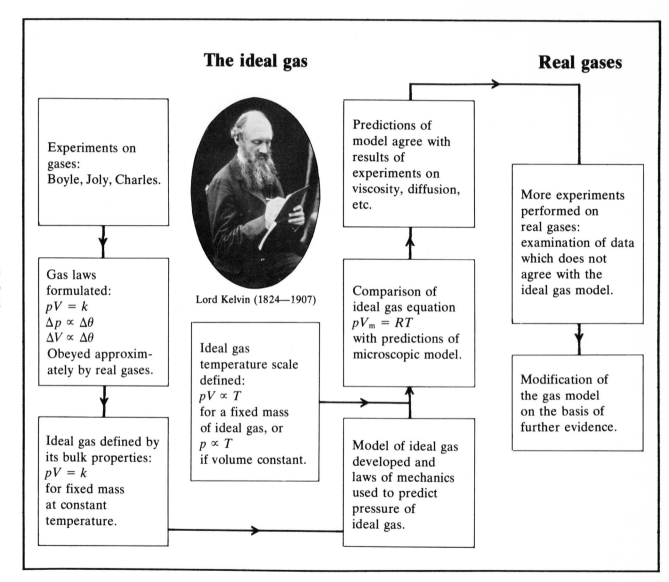

The ideal gas

Real gases

Experiments on gases:
Boyle, Joly, Charles.

Gas laws formulated:
$pV = k$
$\Delta p \propto \Delta \theta$
$\Delta V \propto \Delta \theta$
Obeyed approximately by real gases.

Ideal gas defined by its bulk properties:
$pV = k$
for fixed mass at constant temperature.

Lord Kelvin (1824—1907)

Ideal gas temperature scale defined:
$pV \propto T$
for a fixed mass of ideal gas, or
$p \propto T$
if volume constant.

Predictions of model agree with results of experiments on viscosity, diffusion, etc.

Comparison of ideal gas equation
$pV_m = RT$
with predictions of microscopic model.

Model of ideal gas developed and laws of mechanics used to predict pressure of ideal gas.

More experiments performed on real gases: examination of data which does not agree with the ideal gas model.

Modification of the gas model on the basis of further evidence.

Objectives

When you have completed the work in this chapter you should be able to:

1   Use the following scientific terms correctly:
root mean square speed, distribution curve, isothermal change, adiabatic change, reversible change, change of state of a gas, molar gas constant, principal molar heat capacities, ratio of principal molar heat capacities of a gas.

2   Derive an expression for the pressure of an ideal gas in terms of its density and the mean square speed of its molecules. Show how this is related to the equation of state of the gas.

3   Describe graphically the distribution of molecular speeds in a gas and interpret temperature in terms of molecular kinetic energy.

4   (a) Describe experimental investigations of (i) the variation of pressure of a gas with temperature at constant volume, (ii) the variation of volume of a gas with temperature at constant pressure.
(b) Show how the results agree with the ideal gas equation at low pressures.

5   Describe ways of changing the internal energy of a gas and show that the molar heat capacity at constant pressure is greater than the molar heat capacity at constant volume.

6   Solve problems to determine p, V, T or the r.m.s. speed of gas molecules for an ideal gas, given relevant data.

7   Define and use the following scientific terms and recall their standard symbols and units:
molar heat capacity at constant volume, C_V; molar heat capacity at constant pressure, C_p.

8   Evaluate $(C_p - C_V)$ for an ideal gas.

9   State and use Dalton's law of partial pressures.

10   EXTENSION
Evaluate C_p/C_V for an ideal gas, and solve problems involving the calculation of p, V or T for a gas undergoing adiabatic changes.

11   EXTENSION
Derive an expression for the mean free path of a molecule.

12   EXTENSION
Use the kinetic theory model of a gas to account for the work done in expansion and to provide simple explanations of diffusion and viscosity.

Experiments in chapter 3

TP4 Effect of pressure on the volume of a gas at constant temperature
(1 hour)
TP5 Measurement of temperature by a gas thermometer
(1 hour)

References

Adkins	Chapter 3
Duncan FWA	Chapter 9
Hands	Chapters 3, 5, 6 and 9
Millar	Chapter 10
Nelkon	Chapters 10 and 11
Thorning	Chapters 1, 2, 3 and 4
Whelan	Chapters 24 and 25

3.1 The kinetic theory model of an ideal gas

In this chapter we shall develop a model of the *microscopic* behaviour of the molecules of a gas and we shall relate this model to the behaviour of large amounts of gas (the *macroscopic* behaviour), by studying the *bulk properties* such as pressure, temperature, and rate of diffusion. We cannot study the behaviour of individual molecules but, because we are dealing with large numbers of molecules, we can assume that the bulk properties are governed by the average behaviour of a very large number of molecules.

The opening page of the chapter gives a summary of the development of the study of gases. It will also serve as a guide to the work in chapters 3 and 4. It illustrates how experimental results have been used to suggest a possible model and how the model has been tested and modified in the light of subsequent experimental evidence. Notice also how the study of real gases led to the concept of an ideal gas.

The ideal gas is defined as a gas for which Boyle's law is exactly true for all temperatures and pressures.

Gay-Lussac and Charles both investigated the change in volume of different gases expanding at constant pressure between the ice point (0 °C) and steam point (100 °C). It was found that V_{100}/V_0 was the same for all gases (within the limits of experimental error) and was 1.37 (which is, significantly, 373/273). Joly found that the pressure of gases heated at constant volume changed in an identical way. This led to the idea of an ideal gas temperature scale, defined so that p must be proportional to T at constant volume. So for an ideal gas $pV \propto T$, but we cannot prove this by experiment since it incorporates our definition of temperature.

Q **3.1 Self-assessment question**
Use the definition of an ideal gas to suggest answers to the following questions. Give a reason for each answer.
(a) Would an ideal gas always have the same volume as its container, however large or small?
(b) Could an ideal gas be turned into a liquid, by cooling or by increasing the pressure? ∎

Many properties of matter, like the strength and elasticity of solids and the surface tension of liquids, have been explained by assuming attraction and repulsion forces between molecules. In a gas the molecules have random motion, and the average distance between molecules is very large compared with the range of these intermolecular forces. In an ideal gas we assume that the effect of the attractive forces can be neglected and that the repulsive forces which cause atoms to bounce off each other act only for an instant (i.e. repulsive forces have zero range).

If we assume that the gas is in thermal equilibrium with its container, then the total energy of the gas molecules is constant and, on average, we can consider the collisions of molecules with one another and with the walls to be perfectly elastic.

Q **3.2 Study question**
Make a list of the basic assumptions of the kinetic theory for an ideal gas. ∎

A gas molecule may undergo about 10^{10} collisions per second, having its velocity changed at each collision. The law of conservation of momentum applies to all these collisions. Now consider how the collision process affects the kinetic energies which different molecules have.

Q 3.3 Self-assessment question

Will collisions between molecules result, on average, in higher energy molecules gaining more energy and lower energy molecules losing some of the energy which they have? Don't give a written answer. Think about collisions you have studied between bodies of roughly equal mass and check your answer with the one given at the end of the Unit.■

Q 3.4 Self-assssssment question

Would you expect the process of energy transfer by collision to result in all the molecules having the same speed?■

Since so many collisions occur in the same short time interval, we can assume that whenever one molecule A has its velocity c_1 changed to some other value, another collision is resulting in some other molecule B acquiring velocity c_1 (figure 3.1). This means that when we are considering the effect produced by all the molecules of a gas (the bulk properties) we can ignore intermolecular collisions and consider that each molecule travels at a constant speed in a particular direction until it collides with the molecules of the container.

If the temperature is steady then the total kinetic energy of the molecules will be constant. Although the molecules will have a wide range of speeds, we can assume that the number of molecules within one narrow range of speeds will remain constant.

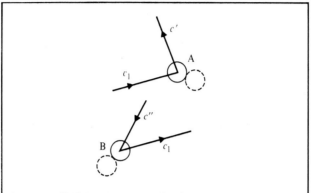

Figure 3.1 Collisions between molecules

Q 3.5 Self-assessment question

Consider eight molecules, each of mass m, with speeds 1,1,2,2,2,3,3 and 4 km s^{-1} respectively.
(a) Calculate the mean or average speed $\bar{c}$.
(b) Calculate the total kinetic energy of the molecules in terms of m.
(c) If all the molecules had the same speed, what value of this speed would give the same total kinetic energy?
(d) You found the speed in part (c) by taking the square root of the average of all the speeds squared, hence it is called the root mean square speed, written $c_{r.m.s.}$ or $\sqrt{\bar{c^2}}$. Check that $c_{r.m.s.}$ is

$$\sqrt{\frac{(2 \times 1^2) + (3 \times 2^2) + (2 \times 3^2) + (1 \times 4^2)}{8}} \times 10^3 \text{ m s}^{-1}$$

(e) Suppose that a gas contains r groups of molecules, N_1 molecules with speed c_1, N_2 with speed c_2, . . . N_r with speed c_r. Write down an expression for $c_{r.m.s.}$ for this gas.■

3.2 The pressure of an ideal gas

There are many ways of obtaining an expression for the pressure of an ideal gas in terms of molecular speed. One approach is shown here as a development question and an alternative proof may be examined in the study question which follows. You only need to know one proof.

Q 3.6 Development question*

Suppose N molecules of an ideal gas, each of mass m, are contained in a sphere of radius r. Figure 3.2 shows the path of one molecule travelling with speed c_1 and rebounding elastically from the inside of the sphere at points P,Q and R.

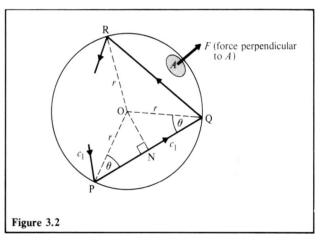

Figure 3.2

(a) Write down an expression for the length PN in terms of θ and r.
(b) Write down an expression for the length PQ in terms of θ and r.
(c) What is the length of QR?
(d) What is the time taken for a molecule to travel from P to Q with speed c_1 after colliding elastically at P?

(e) It takes the same time to travel from Q to R as from P to Q (because PQ = QR). How many collisions does the molecule make with the wall in 1 second?

(f) If there are N_1 molecules with speed c_1 rebounding at angle θ from the wall of the sphere, how many collisions do these N_1 molecules make with the wall in time t?

(g) A proportion of these collisions will occur with the small area A on the surface of the sphere. How many collisions will the N_1 molecules make with area A in time t?

(h) Figure 3.3 shows the component velocities of a molecule before and after collision. The velocity perpendicular to the reflecting wall has changed from $c_1 \cos \theta$ to $-c_1 \cos \theta$. What is the change in momentum perpendicular to the wall due to one collision?

(i) At each collision on A an impulse is given to A. These impulses add up to give a force F acting outwards. F is equal to the change in momentum per second perpendicular to A. What force F acts outwards on A due to the collisions of N_1 molecules?

(j) A force F acting on A produces a pressure, and the same pressure acts all round the sphere. What is the pressure due to the collisions of N_1 molecules with the walls?

(k) There are N molecules in the container; N_1 molecules with speed c_1, N_2 molecules with speed c_2, etc. Show that the total pressure p exerted by the gas is given by the expression

$$p = \frac{1}{3} \frac{m N \overline{c^2}}{V}$$

where V is the volume of the container and $\sqrt{\overline{c^2}}$ is the r.m.s. speed.

(l) Hence show that $p = \frac{1}{3} \rho \overline{c^2}$, where ρ is the density of the gas. ■

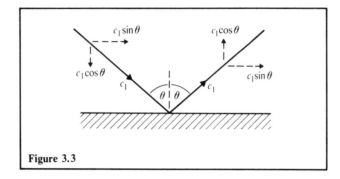

Figure 3.3

Q **3.7 Study question**
Deduce the equation relating pressure and r.m.s. speed by considering an ideal gas in a rectangular box with sides of lengths a, b and l. ■

Q **3.8 Self-assessment question**
(a) Assuming the density of air is 1.29 kg m^{-3} at 273 K and a pressure of 1.00 x 10^5 Pa, what is the value of the r.m.s. speed at this temperature?
(b) Write down an expression for the density of air at 1.00 x 10^5 Pa and 373 K and hence calculate the r.m.s. speed at this temperature.
(c) The density of hydrogen at 273 K and pressure 1.00 $\times$ 10^5 Pa is 9.0 $\times$ 10^{-2} kg m^{-3}. What is the r.m.s. speed of hydrogen molecules at 273 K? ■

The speed of molecules in various gases has been measured directly and agrees well with values calculated from the formula. The fact that the speed of sound in a gas is of the same order of magnitude as molecular speeds also gives further support to this theory.

Q **3.9 Self-assessment question**
In which gas do you predict sound will have the greater speed – air or hydrogen? Give a reason for your answer. ■

E **Experiment TP4**
Effect of pressure on the volume of a gas at constant temperature
In this experiment you will measure changes in the volume of air enclosed in a gas syringe when the pressure acting on the gas changes.

3.3 Molecular speeds and temperature

The graph (figure 3.4) is a distribution curve of molecular speeds in a gas at a certain temperature. (Appendix 1 gives an explanation of distribution curves. You should refer to this now.) The area of any strip under the curve represents the number of molecules in that particular speed range. The total area under the curve represents the total number of molecules being observed.

Q 3.10 Self-assessment question
In figure 3.4, r represents the r.m.s. speed of the molecules and the other speeds indicated are (i) the most probable speed, and (ii) the mean speed. Suggest which of these speeds is represented by p, and which by q. Give reasons for your choice.■

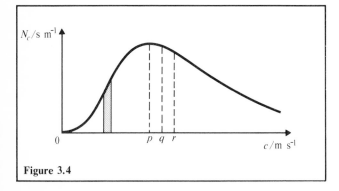

Figure 3.4

AV TP1 Filmloop
Maxwellian speed distribution
The loop shows how pucks moving in random motion simulate molecules in a gas.

Measurement of molecular speeds
Figure 3.5 shows an apparatus used by Zartmann for measuring the distribution of molecular speeds in a gas.

Q 3.11 Study question
Make notes on the Zartmann experiment and use figure 3.5 to explain how the distribution graphs were obtained.■

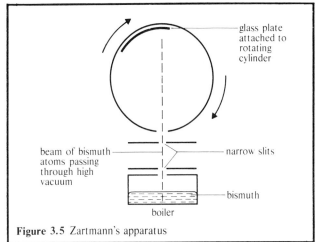

Figure 3.5 Zartmann's apparatus

Q 3.12 Self-assessment question
Figure 3.6 shows how the molecular speed distribution changes with temperature, where $T_1 < T_2 < T_3$. If the temperature is increased, what happens to
(a) the value of the most probable speed,
(b) the number of molecules with speeds greater than c_0,
(c) the proportion of molecules with speeds near the mean speed?■

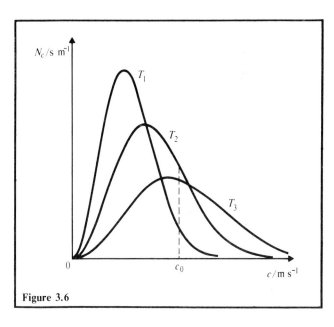

Figure 3.6

Interpretation of temperature

How is the temperature of a gas related to the molecular model? Let us consider gases at the same temperature, and the relationship between the ideal gas temperature scale and the energy of gas molecules.

If we have two ideal gases, A and B, at the *same temperature*, mixing them up will produce no change of temperature in either gas. Although molecules of A collide with molecules of B, there is no net transfer of energy as a result of these collisions.

By studying the mechanics of large numbers of identical particles, it can be shown that if there is no net transfer of energy between two types of particles, then the mean *translational* kinetic energies of the two types are equal. (*Translation* means movement of the whole molecule through space, as distinct from rotation of the molecule.) The molecules of gases A and B must therefore have the same average kinetic energy of translation.

For two gases A and B at the same temperature,

$$\frac{1}{2} m_A \overline{c_A^2} = \frac{1}{2} m_B \overline{c_B^2}$$

Q 3.13 Self-assessment question

The mass of an oxygen molecule is sixteen times the mass of a hydrogen molecule. What is the ratio of the r.m.s. speed of oxygen to the r.m.s. speed of hydrogen at the same temperature?■

Q 3.14 Development question*

Suppose two gases at the same temperature occupy the same volume V and exert equal pressures p.
(a) Write out and then complete the equations

$$pV = \underline{\quad} m_1 \underline{\quad} \overline{c_1^2} = \underline{\quad}\underline{\quad}\underline{\quad} \overline{c_2^2}$$

(b) Write down an equation, in terms of the mean square molecular speeds, to express the fact that the two gases are at the same temperature.
(c) What can you conclude from the equations in (a) and (b)?■

Equal volumes of gases at the same temperature and pressure contain equal numbers of molecules. This is a statement of Avogadro's law. (Appendix 2 revises the concept of the mole and the Avogadro constant N_A.)

We have seen how thermal equilibrium between gases is determined by the molecular kinetic energy. Can we go further and interpret temperature as a measure of the mean translational kinetic energy of the molecules?

If we assume that $\frac{1}{2} m \overline{c^2} \propto T$ we can write

$$\frac{1}{2} m \overline{c^2} = \frac{3}{2} kT$$

(The reason for choosing $\frac{3}{2} k$ as the constant will appear later.)

Temperature on the ideal gas scale is defined from $pV \propto T$, and leads to the equation $pV_m = RT$ for 1 mole where R is the molar gas constant, 8.3 J mol^{-1} K^{-1}.

Q 3.15 Development question*

(a) Write an equation for pV, where V is the volume occupied by N molecules of a gas, in terms of R and T.
(b) Write an equation for pV (for N molecules) in terms of the mean square speed of the molecules.
(c) Use your equation in (b) to relate pV to T, assuming $\frac{1}{2} m \overline{c^2} = \frac{3}{2} kT$.■

The equations obtained in parts (a) and (c) are identical if $k = R/N_A$. k is called the Boltzmann constant.■

So the interpretation of temperature as a measure of the mean molecular translational energy of an ideal gas is consistent with the definition of temperature on the ideal gas scale (i.e. from the bulk properties of the ideal gas). The average translational kinetic energy of the individual molecules is equal to $\frac{3}{2}kT$.

Q 3.16 Self-assessment question

(a) Write down an expression for the total translational kinetic energy per mole of gas in terms of R and T. How does this vary from one gas to another?
(b) Express $c_{r.m.s.}$ in terms of R, T and M_m (the molar mass); hence evaluate $c_{r.m.s.}$ for hydrogen at 273 K. Does your answer agree with that for question 3.8 (c) if, for hydrogen, $M_m = 0.002$ kg mol^{-1}?■

Q 3.17 Self-assessment question

(a) Use values of R and N_A to calculate the Boltzmann constant k. Hence calculate the *average* translational kinetic energy of the individual molecules of a gas at 300 K.
(b) Is this value the same for molecules of any gas?
(c) What would be the mass of a molecule whose r.m.s. speed is 500 m s^{-1} at 300 K?■

E Experiment TP5
Measurement of temperature by a gas thermometer

A simple constant volume gas thermometer is calibrated at the ice and steam points and then used to measure the temperature of the room and of a solution of brine.

Q 3.18 Study question

State Dalton's law of partial pressures and say how it can be derived from the assumptions of the kinetic theory.■

SYLLABUS EXTENSION

3.4 The kinetic theory explains other gas properties

The kinetic theory provides an explanation of many important properties of gases and the model proves a very valuable one since its predictions agree with important laws discovered experimentally.

Diffusion

This term is used to describe the intermingling of different types of gas molecules to produce a uniform distribution in a container, but it is also used to describe the process of escape of gas molecules from a container, through a small hole or a porous wall (a process sometimes called effusion). The probability of a molecule escaping through a small hole in a given time will depend on the mean speed of the molecules.

Q 3.19 Study question

If a mixture of gases A and B is in a container with a porous wall, use the kinetic theory to show that

$$\frac{\lambda_A}{\lambda_B} = \sqrt{\frac{M_B}{M_A}}$$

where λ_A and λ_B are the rates of escape of molecules A and B and M_A and M_B are the molecular masses. What assumptions did you make?■

Q 3.20 Study question

Explain why the smell of a gas travels relatively slowly whilst the molecules move at very high speeds. Include in your answer terms like 'random collision course' and 'mean free path.'■

The *mean free path* is the average distance a molecule travels between collisions. An estimate of the mean free path can be obtained by observing the rate at which the brown colour of bromine vapour moves up a tube of air when liquid bromine is allowed to evaporate in the tube. In the next question you can use some typical results from a bromine diffusion experiment, together with a calculated value of the r.m.s. speed, to find the mean free path.

Q 3.21 Development question*

(a) Calculate the r.m.s. speed of bromine molecules if the density of bromine at a temperature of 290 K and a pressure of 10^5 Pa is 7.5 kg m^{-3}.
(b) What is the total path length of a molecule travelling at this speed for 500 seconds?
(c) If the molecule takes N short paths of average length λ between collisions, what is λN after 500 s?
(d) The progress of a molecule on a random collision course can be shown to be $\lambda \sqrt{N}$ after N random steps. By observing the movement of the brown vapour during a bromine diffusion experiment, the random progress of bromine molecules was found to be 0.1 m after 500 seconds. Express this result in an equation.
(e) Use the information from (c) and (d) to calculate the mean free path λ.■

Q 3.22 Study question

Two molecules will collide if their motions bring their centres within one molecular *diameter* of one another (figure 3.7). Show that the mean free path of a molecule in an ideal gas is given by $\lambda = 1/(n\pi\sigma^2)$ where n is the number of molecules per unit volume and σ is the molecular diameter.■

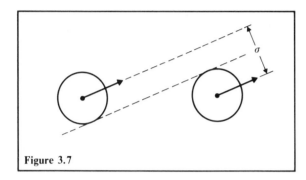

Figure 3.7

Viscous forces in a moving gas

The kinetic theory provides a way of understanding the forces which act when different parts of a fluid (gas or liquid) are in relative motion. The molecular speeds calculated above are the random speeds determined by temperature. If the whole gas is moving in a particular direction, each molecule will have a speed which is the resultant of this *directed* speed and its *random* speed.

Q 3.23 Development question*

Figure 3.8 shows two layers of gas. Layer A is travelling faster than layer B.
(a) In which layer do the molecules, on average, possess the greater speeds?

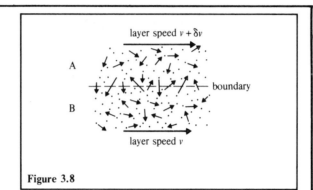

Figure 3.8

(b) Is there any change of momentum across the boundary between A and B due to molecules crossing the boundary? Give a reason for your answer.
(c) What effect will the transfer of momentum across the boundary between A and B tend to have on the relative velocities of layers A and B?■

The force which opposes the relative motion of layers A and B is called a viscous force and acts along the boundary of the two layers. The viscous force is the result of the momentum transfer across the boundary and is equal to the rate of change of momentum.

Q 3.24 Self-assessment question

How will the viscous force depend on
(a) the area of the boundary between A and B,
(b) the difference in velocity between layers A and B?■

SYLLABUS EXTENSION

Low gas pressures

The following questions are about the design of a pump for obtaining low pressures in a gas and the measurement of low gas pressures.

Q 3.25 Development question

Figure 3.9 shows a rotary vacuum pump in three positions during a cycle. The pump consists of a cylindrical chamber in which a rotating cylinder is mounted off-centre. Two vanes B and C are spring-loaded and mounted in a slot in the rotating cylinder so that they divide the pump chamber into two separate compartments throughout the rotation. D is an outlet valve, and the whole pump is immersed in a bath of oil. Use the diagram to explain how gas can be exhausted from a container, by considering changes in the part of the chamber marked A during one cycle.■

Q 3.26 Study question

Make notes on the principle of operation of the McLeod gauge for measuring very low gas pressures.■

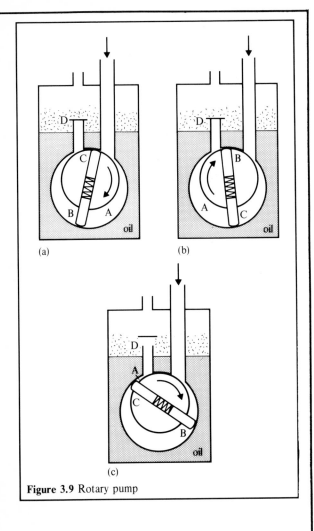

(a)

(b)

(c)

Figure 3.9 Rotary pump

3.5 Changing the energy of an ideal gas

Applying the first law of thermodynamics to an ideal gas,

$$\text{heat supplied} = \frac{\text{work done}}{\text{by the gas}} + \frac{\text{increase in internal}}{\text{energy of the gas}}$$

$$Q = W + \Delta U$$

When the pressure, volume and temperature of a gas change, we say the *state* of the gas has changed. For a particular state, the gas has a fixed amount of internal energy (we say internal energy U is a function of state). The change in internal energy ΔU depends only on the intial and final states of the gas (i.e. on the initial and final values of p, V, and T). The law relating to a change of state is called an *equation of state*. $pV = nRT$ is the equation of state of an ideal gas. You will encounter other equations of state for real gases in chapter 4.

Sometimes, change of state is used to describe the change of a substance from liquid to solid: this change would be more correctly described as a *change of phase* from liquid phase to solid phase since change of state is a more general phrase which could also apply to a gas doubling its volume.

In an ideal gas, we assume that there is no molecular attraction and that the internal energy of the gas will not depend on the separation of the molecules (i.e. internal energy is independent of the volume occupied by an ideal gas).

So for an ideal gas, internal energy U is determined only by its temperature. A change in internal energy ΔU is determined by the temperature change, and if there is no temperature change, there is no change in internal energy.

Work done by an expanding gas

Q 3.27 Development question*

A gas at pressure p is given a tiny supply of energy which enables it to expand very slowly by an amount δV by pushing a frictionless piston, as illustrated in figure 3.10.

(a) What force is required to push the piston back?

(b) Show that the work done by the gas is $p\,\delta V$ when the volume increases by δV.

(c) Show that this expression has the units of energy.

(d) What has been assumed about the pressure during this small expansion δV?

(e) How can this amount of work $p\,\delta V$ be represented on a graph of p against V, such as that shown in figure 3.11?

(f) How can the work done by the gas in expanding by δV be represented if the pressure varies along the curve shown?

(g) How can the work done be represented graphically if the gas expands from volume V_1 to volume V_2 (i) when the state of the gas changes along the curve shown, from state A to state F, (ii) when the pressure remains constant during the expansion?■

3.28 Self-assessment question

Suppose a gas changes from state A (at which the temperature is T_A) to some other state B (at which the temperature is T_B). Two different ways in which the change can take place are shown in figure 3.12.

(a) What can you say about the work done by the gas in each of the two changes?

(b) What can you say about the change in internal energy of the gas in each change?

(c) What can be deduced about the heat transfer to or from the gas in each change?■

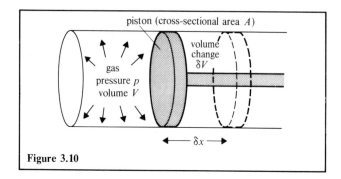

Figure 3.10

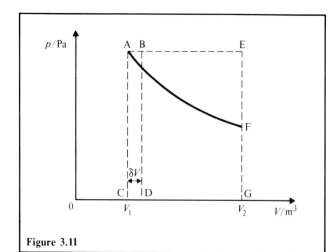

Figure 3.11

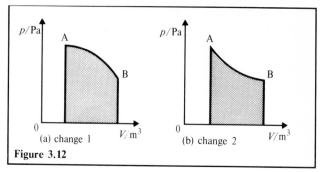

Figure 3.12

Note: In answering this question you have assumed that the expansion takes place infinitely slowly so that the temperature and pressure are in equilibrium throughout the gas and have a determinable value. (In a rapid expansion, the pressure and temperature will not be uniform throughout the gas and there will be no means of finding the values of p and T in different parts of the gas.) Such an infinitely slow expansion in a frictionless container is a *reversible process*.

Q 3.29 Self-assessment question

Explain the term 'reversible process' and say what is true of energy changes for any reversible process.■

Isothermal change

This means a change at the same temperature. For isothermal expansion of an ideal gas, since there is no temperature change there is no change in internal energy, therefore $\Delta U = 0$ and $Q = W$. Heat Q must be supplied to provide energy W to enable the gas to do work in expanding.

Q 3.30 Self-assessment question
What relationship between pressure and volume is applicable to an isothermal change?■

EXTENSION

Q 3.31 Study question
(a) Deduce an expression for the work done during isothermal expansion.
(b) Show that the work done when a gas expands to double its volume under isothermal conditions is $nRT \ln 2$, where n (moles) is the amount of gas.■

Adiabatic change

This occurs when no heat enters or leaves the system during the change. In this case $Q = 0$ and $W = \Delta U$. It can be realised in a well lagged container, or if the change occurs so rapidly that there is no time for any heat exchange to occur.

Q 3.32 Self-assessment question
If a gas is compressed adiabatically what will happen to its temperature? Give a reason for your answer.■

Isothermal and adiabatic changes are the extreme kinds of change. More commonly, changes will occur in which the temperature changes *and* energy is exchanged with the surroundings.

Q 3.33 Self-assessment question
Why is it impossible in practice to achieve either isothermal or adiabatic change. Suggest a reason for each case.■

Q 3.34 Self-assessment question
If a car tyre is suddenly punctured, how would you describe the kind of change which occurs in the gas? What kind of temperature change would you expect?■

Q 3.35 Self-assessment question
Figure 3.13 shows three graphs representing isothermal processes for a given mass of ideal gas (i.e. three graphs of p against V, each at a constant temperature).
(a) Name the law which any one of these curves represents.
(b) What relationship is true for all the points on all three curves?
(c) What law relates the points A, B and C?
(d) If the temperature T_2 is 300 K, what are the other temperatures?
(e) If the gas expands adiabatically from state B, which curve represents a possible adiabatic process, BE_1 or BE_2? Give a reason.

(f) If the molar mass of this gas is 3.2×10^{-2} kg mol^{-1}, what mass of gas do these curves apply to?
($R = 8.3$ J mol^{-1} K^{-1})
(g) How much energy is needed to take the gas from state A to state D at constant pressure?■

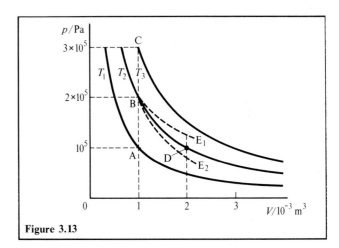

Figure 3.13

Q 3.36 Study question

The relationship between pressure and volume during a reversible adiabatic expansion of an ideal gas is given by the equation pV^γ = constant (γ is the ratio of the principal molar heat capacities of a gas, as explained in section 3.6). For all possible changes pV/T remains constant. Use these relationships to find equations relating, for an adiabatic change,

(a) V and T, and
(b) p and T.■

Q 3.37 Self-assessment question

Show, with the help of a graph of p against V, that the work done in a reversible isothermal expansion is greater than the work done in a reversible adiabatic expansion (for the same volume change).■

Q 3.38 Self-assessment question

(a) What change in temperature will be produced if an ideal gas at pressure 10^5 Pa and temperature 300 K changes its volume from 1000 cm^3 to 2000 cm^3 by a reversible adiabatic expansion ($\gamma = 1.4$)?
(b) What is the pressure after the expansion?■

3.6 Molar heat capacities of a gas

Suppose we add heat Q to an amount of gas n (moles) and, as a result, its temperature rises by ΔT. The temperature rise will depend on how much energy is used in doing external work (e.g. by the gas moving the walls of its container). This means that a gas has a multitude of different values for the heat needed to raise the temperature of 1 mole through 1 K. That is, a gas has an infinite number of molar heat capacities.

Two special conditions are chosen to define the two *principal* molar heat capacities, (a) heating at constant volume and (b) heating at constant pressure. The symbols C_V and C_p are used for these principal molar heat capacities.

Q 3.39 Self-assessment question

(a) Define C_V and state its unit.
(b) Write an equation relating Q, the heat input to an amount of gas n (moles), with ΔT, the temperature rise at constant volume.
(c) What is the value of ΔU, the increase in internal energy?■

Q 3.40 Development question*

(a) Write down an expression in terms of R for the total kinetic energy of an amount n (moles) of an ideal monatomic gas at temperature (i) T, and (ii) $T + \Delta T$.
(b) What change in total kinetic energy occurs when the temperature of this amount of gas is increased by ΔT?
(c) Deduce the molar heat capacity at constant volume.
(d) What does the theory predict for the numerical value of C_V? Does the data given in table 3.1 agree with this prediction for any gas?■

Table 3.1

Gas	$C_V/$ J mol^{-1} K^{-1}	$C_p/$ J mol^{-1} K^{-1}	$(C_p - C_V)/$ J mol^{-1} K^{-1}	γ
H$_2$	20.1	28.4	8.3	1.41
He	12.6	21.0	8.3	1.66
Ar	12.4	20.8	8.4	1.67
Ne	12.7	21.3	8.3	1.64
O$_2$	20.8	29.1	8.3	1.40
CO$_2$	28.2	36.5	8.3	1.25
ether	129	139	10	1.08

If an amount n (moles) of gas is heated through ΔT at constant pressure, it will expand. The heat Q supplied will increase the temperature and also do work in expanding the gas against the constant pressure.

Q 3.41 Development question*

(a) Write down equations relating Q with C_p and ΔU with C_V.
(b) Substitute these expressions into the equation for the first law of thermodynamics.
(c) Hence obtain an expression for $(C_p - C_V)$. ■

Your answer to question 3.41(c) indicates that C_p is always greater than C_V by the amount of external work done per mole per kelvin temperature rise.

The ratio of the principal molar heat capacities C_p/C_V is given the symbol γ, and γ must always be greater than 1.

EXTENSION

Q 3.42 Study question

Use the expression obtained for $(C_p - C_V)$ and your answer to question 3.40(d) to obtain a value for γ for a monatomic gas. ■

Table 3.1 gives experimental values of molar heat capacities, and the values of $(C_p - C_V)$ and γ calculated from them.

The kinetic theory predicts that for monatomic gases $C_V = 3R/2$, $(C_p - C_V) = R$ and $\gamma = 1.66$.

This theory has so far considered gas particles as point masses whose only internal energy is kinetic energy of translation – an assumption which is acceptable for monatomic gases. However, diatomic and triatomic molecules can have energy due to rotation. When a gas is heated, the internal energy acquired will be shared amongst different kinds of motion. This accounts for the higher value of C_V for gases with more complex molecules and the correspondingly smaller value of γ.

Comprehension exercise

THE PHYSICAL STATE OF STELLAR MATTER

(Adapted from *The stars: their structure and evolution* by R. J. Tayler, Vol. 10 of Wykeham Science Series for schools and universities.)

The balance between gravitational attraction and thermal pressure plays the principal role in determining the structure of a star. In the early years of the study of stellar structure there was much discussion about the physical state of matter in stars. It was thought that the stars could not be solid because their temperatures were so high and that they could not be gaseous because their mean densities were too high (e.g. at a typical point in the sun the temperature is $\sim 2 \times 10^6$ K and the concentration of particles is $\sim 2 \times 10^{30}$ m^{-3}). It is now believed that stars are composed of an almost perfect gas in most circumstances. This almost perfect gas is, however, unusual in two respects.

The more important respect is that the stellar material is an ionised gas or *plasma*. The temperature inside stars is so high that all but the most tightly bound electrons are separated from the atoms. This makes possible a very much greater compression of the stellar material without deviation from the perfect gas law because a nuclear dimension is 10^{-15} m compared with a typical atomic dimension of 10^{-10} m. The word plasma is the name given to a quantity of ionised gas. It has been recognised in recent years that a plasma can be regarded as a fourth phase of matter and that most of the material in the universe is in this fourth phase.

The second important difference between most laboratory conditions and conditions in stars is that radiation is in thermal equilibrium with matter in stellar interiors, and its intensity is governed by Planck's law. Just as the particles in a gas exert a pressure which can be calculated from the kinetic theory of gases by considering collisions of particles with an imaginary surface in the gas, the photons exert a pressure known as radiation pressure. If β is the fraction of the total pressure, p, contributed by gas pressure towards opposing gravitational contraction then $(1 - \beta)$ is the fraction contributed by radiation pressure. At one time it was thought that radiation pressure was of comparable importance to gas pressure in ordinary stars. It is now realised that although there are some exceptional stars in which radiation pressure is of vital importance, it is only of marginal importance in most stars.

From the kinetic theory of gases, the pressure of a perfect gas can be shown to have the form:

$$p_{gas} = nkT \tag{1}$$

where n is the number of particles per cubic metre and k is Boltzmann's constant (1.38×10^{-23} J K^{-1}).

The corresponding expression for radiation pressure is:

$$p_{rad} = \frac{1}{3} \alpha T^4 \tag{2}$$

where α is the radiation density constant, which is 7.55×10^{-16} J m^{-3} K^{-4}.

Questions

1   What force compresses the stellar material and what force prevents the stellar material from condensing completely?

2   Explain what you understand by the phrase 'stars are composed of an almost perfect gas'.

3   Why is stellar material considered to exist as a plasma rather than in one of the other three phases of matter? Explain how this fourth phase of matter is produced.

4   Calculate the root mean square speed of protons at a typical point in the sun if the mass of a proton is 1.67×10^{-27} kg.

5   Discuss how the postulates of the simple kinetic theory of gases apply to a star which is composed of a fully ionised gas (hydrogen) at high temperatures.

6   Explain in your own words what is meant by radiation pressure. Compare numerically the radiation pressure and gas pressure at a typical point in the sun. Comment briefly on your result.

7   From the passage it can be deduced that the total pressure, $p = \alpha T^4/3(1 - \beta)$. By a similar process of reasoning involving equation (1) deduce another equation for p and hence use the two equations to obtain for the total pressure an expression in which temperature does not appear.

Questions on objectives

1   Explain why the molecules of a gas do not all move with the same speed. Explain what is meant by r.m.s. speed.

(objective 1)

2   Derive an expression for the pressure exerted by an ideal gas in terms of its density and the root mean square speed of its molecules.

(objective 2)

3   What is the interpretation of temperature given by the kinetic theory of gases? Show how this interpretation is used to predict, from the equation derived in question 2, that pV_m/T is a universal constant for a mole of any gas. What is the unit of this constant?

(objective 3)

4   Explain how the simple kinetic theory of gases agrees with the experimental result that the pressure of a fixed mass of gas at constant temperature is inversely proportional to its volume.

(objective 4)

5   Distinguish between adiabatic and isothermal change and explain why there is a change in temperature when a gas expands adiabatically against an external pressure.

(objectives 1 and 5)

6   Calculate the r.m.s. speed of oxygen molecules at $27\,°C$, given that the r.m.s. speed of hydrogen molecules at $0\,°C$ is $1.84 \times 10^3\,m\,s^{-1}$. Assume the gases behave like ideal gases and that the relative molecular masses of hydrogen and oxygen are 2 and 32 respectively.

(objective 6)

7   A vessel of volume $0.050\,m^3$ is filled with helium at a temperature of 300 K. If the pressure exerted by the gas is $1.0 \times 10^5\,Pa$, calculate
(a)   the mass of helium,
(b)   the root mean square speed of the helium atoms.
Assume the molar mass of helium is $0.0040\,kg\,mol^{-1}$ and that the gas constant R is $8.3\,J\,mol^{-1}\,K^{-1}$.

(objective 6)

8   State Dalton's law of partial pressures. A mixture of 21 g of nitrogen and 32 g of oxygen is maintained at a pressure of 1 atmosphere. Calculate the partial pressures of each gas.

(objective 9)

9   Explaining each step in your procedure, derive an expression for the difference between the heat capacity at constant volume and the heat capacity at constant pressure for one mole of an ideal gas. Hence obtain a value of γ for an ideal monatomic gas.

(objectives 8 and 10)

10   EXTENSION
A mole of gas is compressed isothermally at temperature T_1 to half its volume and then allowed to expand adiabatically to its original volume.
(a)   In terms of the initial pressure p_1 find (i) the final pressure, (ii) the final temperature T_2. (The ratio of the principal molar heat capacities is 1.4.)
(b)   What energy must be supplied to the gas to heat it back to temperature T_1 at constant volume? Express your answer in terms of the original temperature T_1.

(objective 10)

11   EXTENSION
What is meant by the mean free path of a molecule in a gas? Explain how the mean free path can be estimated in terms of the number of molecules per unit volume and the diameter of a molecule. How do you interpret the term 'diameter' for this purpose?

(objective 11)

12   EXTENSION
Use the kinetic model of a gas to account briefly for
(a)   the cooling of a gas during adiabatic expansion,
(b)   the existence of viscous forces when parts of a gas are in relative motion.

(objective 12)

Chapter

4

Real gases and vapours

Aim

The aim of this chapter is to study the properties of real gases and vapours and to discover to what extent these properties can be predicted and explained on the basis of a simple kinetic theory of matter.

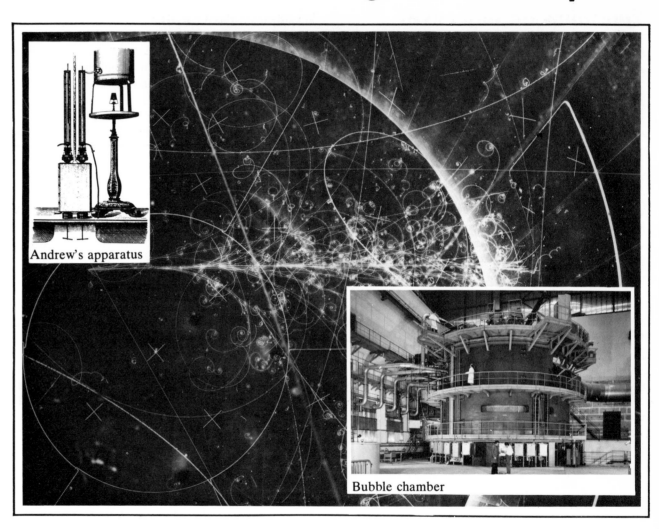

Andrew's apparatus

Bubble chamber

Objectives

When you have completed the work in this chapter you should be able to:

1 Use the following scientific terms correctly: vapour, saturated vapour, nuclei of condensation, vaporisation.

2 Define and use the following scientific terms: critical point, normal boiling point.

3 Use the kinetic theory to account for the pressures exerted at different temperatures by saturated and unsaturated vapours.

4 Describe the relationship between pressure, volume and temperature for real gases and vapours.

5 Describe methods of measuring s.v.p. and account for the variation of boiling point with temperature.

6 Solve problems involving the calculation of the pressure exerted by a mixture of gas and saturated vapour at different temperatures.

7 Describe the principles used in the liquefaction of gases.

8 EXTENSION

Show how van der Waals' equation provides a possible equation of state for real gases.

Experiment in chapter 4

TP 6 Variation of s.v.p. of water with temperature (1 hour)

References

Adkins	Chapter 4
Duncan FWA	Chapter 9
Hands	Chapters 3, 5, 6 and 9
Millar	Chapter 11
Nelkon	Chapters 12 and 13
Thorning	Chapters 5 and 6
Whelan	Chapters 27 and 28

Chapter 4

Study time: 1 week

4.1 Real gases

We have developed a very useful model, the *ideal* gas. It is useful because many gases behave like the model over a wide range of temperatures and pressures. But we haven't yet studied the whole picture. What happens to real gases at very high pressures and low temperatures? We must investigate the properties of real gases and vapours and discover how the kinetic theory of gases can, if necessary, be modified to account for this behaviour. You will discover that the forces between molecules can have an important influence on the behaviour of gases, and you will study the principles involved in turning gases into liquids.

Before examining the experimental evidence about real gases, you can remind yourself of the graphical ways of representing the behaviour of an ideal gas.

Q 4.1 Self-assessment question

Show the relationship between p, V and T for an amount n (moles) of ideal gas by sketching graphs of
(a) p against V at three temperatures T_1, T_2, and T_3, if $T_1 > T_2 > T_3$,
(b) pV against p at temperatures T_1, T_2 and T_3,
(c) pV/nT against p, marking the value of the intercept.■

For gases like hydrogen, oxygen and nitrogen at temperatures around 273 K, the difference between their behaviour and that predicted by the graphs for an ideal gas is less than 0.1% at atmospheric pressure.

But what happens at higher pressures? Figure 4.1 shows the behaviour of these gases at 273 K and pressures up to 1000 times atmospheric pressure. Compare this figure with your answer to question 4.1(c). At **these high pressures**, the deviation from ideal gas behaviour is considerable: for example, the value of pV/nT ranges from 7 to 17 J mol^{-1} K^{-1}, instead of having the value predicted for an ideal gas of 8.3143 J mol^{-1} K^{-1}. However, the enlargement in figure 4.1 is a reminder of the very small percentage deviation at low pressures, which enables Boyle's law to be a useful description of the behaviour of these gases over a considerable pressure range.

Significant progress in the study of gases and vapours resulted from a long series of experiments on the behaviour of carbon dioxide performed between 1863 and 1869 by Thomas Andrews. He studied the relationship between pressure and volume at different temperatures and figure 4.2 is a representation of his apparatus.

Q 4.2 Study question

Use figure 4.2 and your reference texts to answer the following questions.
(a) How was the pressure in Andrews' apparatus varied?
(b) How was the pressure exerted on the carbon dioxide actually measured? What assumption was made about the behaviour of air?
(c) To obtain graphs of p against V at different temperatures, is it necessary to maintain all or only part of the apparatus at these temperatures? Give reasons for your answer.■

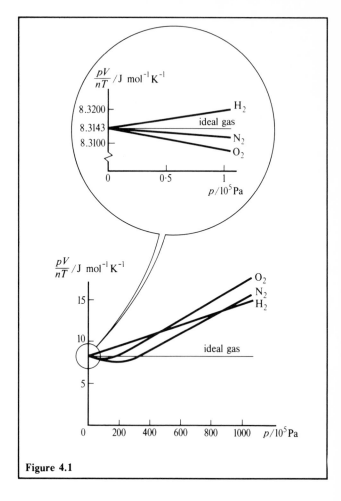

Figure 4.1

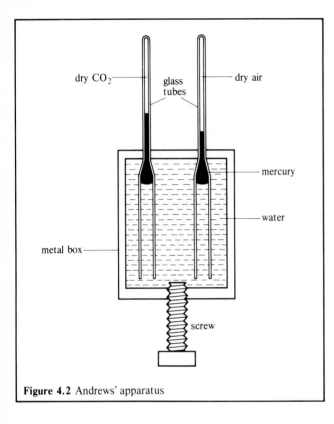

Figure 4.2 Andrews' apparatus

Q 4.3 Development question*

The isothermals obtained in Andrews' experiments are shown in figure 4.3. Make a copy of the diagram.

(a) Mark on your diagram a temperature T_1 for which carbon dioxide seems to behave like an ideal gas. Mark this region of the diagram G, for gas.

(b) Say why the graphs suggest that liquids can be compressed relatively little, and label the region where the carbon dioxide is in the liquid phase L.

(c) What happens in the shaded region? Why does the volume change between A and B although the pressure and temperature remain constant?

(d) The critical temperature T_c is defined as the temperature above which a gas cannot be liquefied by increasing the pressure. Mark the critical isothermal T_c.

(e) A substance in the gaseous phase is called a vapour if it is at a temperature at which it can be liquefied by compression (i.e. below the critical temperature). Label the region of the diagram where carbon dioxide is a vapour V.

(f) Mark an isothermal T_2 which shows a temperature at which carbon dioxide changes from vapour to liquid when the volume is decreasing.

(g) State two reasons why heat must be supplied when the state of the carbon dioxide changes from A to B.■

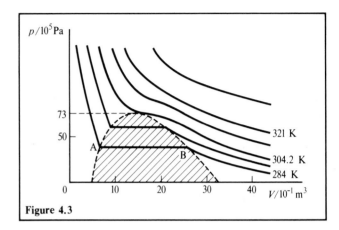

Figure 4.3

p–V–T surfaces

Figure 4.3 shows how p and V depend on each other uniquely for each temperature shown on the graph. The behaviour of the substance can also be shown by other two-dimensional graphs of p against T (at constant volume) and V against T (at constant pressure). All this information can, however, be represented by a single surface, as shown in figures 4.4 and 4.5. These are the three-dimensional plots of p, V, T for an ideal gas (figure 4.4) and a real substance (figure 4.5). These graphs emphasise the fact that once the values of two variables (e.g. p and T) have been fixed, the value of the third variable, V, is determined uniquely by the shape of this surface for a particular substance. Isothermals are marked on the surface in figure 4.5, showing the relationship between p and V at constant temperatures. They include the critical isothermal at T_c. (These lines give graphs like those from Andrews' experiment and you can compare these lines drawn on the surface at T_1 and T_2 with your answer to question 4.3.) The triple line specifies the only temperature and pressure at which a substance can exist in all three phases.

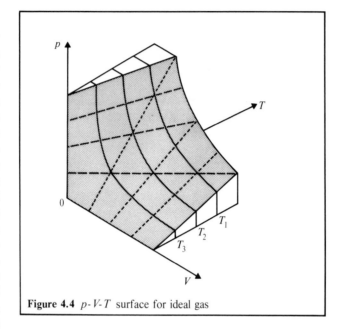

Figure 4.4 p-V-T surface for ideal gas

Q 4.4 Self-assessment question

(a) Sketch a graph of V against T at constant pressure for the substance if it begins as a solid at D (figure 4.5) and the path on the p–V–T surface passes through E and F.

(i) Does the substance expand as a solid when heated?
(ii) What happens to the volume when it melts?
(iii) What is the phase of this substance at E and at F? Explain why no obvious transition from liquid to gas occurs.

(b) What happens to a vapour as the pressure increases at a constant temperature which is below T_{tr}?■

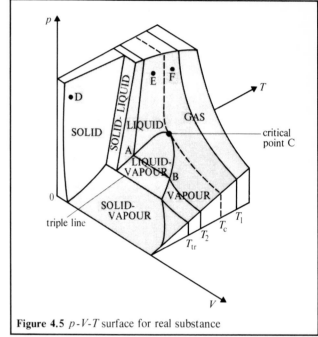

Figure 4.5 p-V-T surface for real substance

Significantly, Andrews titled his research paper of 1869 *On the continuity of the gaseous and liquid states of matter* (Phil. Trans. R. Soc. 159, no. 2,575). He wrote:

'The ordinary gaseous and ordinary liquid states are, in short, only widely separated forms of the same condition of matter, and may be made to pass into one another by a series of gradations so gentle that the passage shall nowhere present any interruption or breach of continuity. From carbonic acid as a perfect gas to carbonic acid as a perfect liquid, the transition we have seen may be accomplished by a continuous process, and the gas and liquid are only distant stages of a long series of continuous physical changes . . .'

The behaviour of nitrogen

Do gases like nitrogen and oxygen behave like carbon dioxide, or is there a fundamental difference between these gases? It was once believed that some gases were 'permanent' gases. However, Andrews' experiments showed that carbon dioxide could be liquefied by compression if the temperature was low enough, and he argued that all gases could be liquefied by compression if the temperature was first reduced below the critical temperature for that substance.

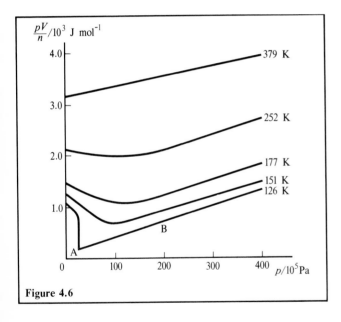

Figure 4.6

Figure 4.6 shows the results obtained from experiments on nitrogen over a wide range of temperatures. Notice the dramatic change in the shape of the graphs as the temperature is lowered.

Q 4.5 Self-assessment question
(a) Part of the graph of pV/n against p at temperature 126 K is vertical. Which of the three quantities, p, V, T, is/are (i) constant, (ii) varying along the vertical line? Explain the vertical portion and say what the phase of nitrogen is between A and B.
(b) The graphs indicate that the critical temperature for nitrogen is between two of the temperatures plotted on the graph. Which two? Give a reason for your answer and check it with the data given in table 4.1.
(c) All gases have a *Boyle temperature* at which the deviation from ideal gas behaviour is a minimum over a wide pressure range. Between which two temperatures plotted on figure 4.6 is the Boyle temperature? Is your answer in agreement with the data in table 4.1?■

The contrasting behaviour of different gases can be predicted if we know the values of the important temperatures shown in table 4.1.

Table 4.1

Gas	Critical temperature T_c/K	Boyle temperature T_B/K	Normal boiling point T/K
He	5	30	4.2
H₂	32	109	20
N₂	127	323	77
O₂	155	423	90
CO₂	304	>600	195

Q 4.6 Self-assessment question
Is it possible
(a) to liquefy oxygen by compression at 0 °C,
(b) to have carbon dioxide gas at −90 °C?
Give a reason for each answer.■

Evidence for intermolecular attraction

All gases condense into a liquid phase if the temperature is low enough. When this happens, the attractive forces between molecules are able to produce a transition to a liquid phase in which there is obvious cohesion between molecules and a liquid surface is formed. Is it possible to find evidence of intermolecular attraction forces in gases at temperatures far above the critical temperature?

In 1845, Joule attempted to find evidence for these intermolecular forces using the apparatus shown in figure 4.7. Gas in A was allowed to expand into the evacuated container B and the whole apparatus was immersed in a water bath. If a gas expands into a vacuum, no external work is done. Is any energy required?

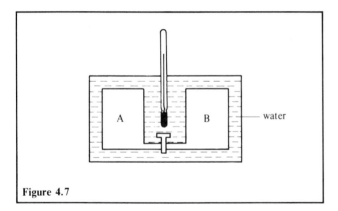

Figure 4.7

If intermolecular attractive forces exist, allowing a gas to expand freely will still require energy, since work will be done against the attractive forces as the molecules separate, giving the molecules greater potential energy.

Q 4.7 Development question*
Apply the first law of thermodynamics to the gas expanding from A into B ($Q = \Delta U + W$).
(a) What energy Q is supplied and what external work W is done?
(b) Show that the internal energy ΔU of the gas is unchanged.
(c) If forces of intermolecular attraction exist, the potential energy of the gas molecules is increased as the gas expands. What would you expect to happen to the kinetic energy of the molecules and the temperature of the gas?■

Joule did not obtain the result he hoped for (this often happens in physics experiments!). There was no change in the water temperature. His conclusion was not that intermolecular forces do not exist but that his thermometer was not sensitive enough and his experiment was badly designed in using the temperature change in a water bath to detect a heat change.

Q 4.8 Self-assessment question
Why do you think the large bath of water made it impossible to detect any temperature change which may have occurred in the gas?■

Joule and Kelvin later collaborated successfully, in 1850, to obtain convincing evidence that intermolecular attractive forces do exist.

SYLLABUS EXTENSION

Q 4.9 Study question
Make brief notes on the Joule-Kelvin porous plug experiment, stating how the temperature of the gas was measured and why a porous plug was used. Summarise the results obtained.■

By 1869, when Andrews published his results on CO_2, the idea of two types of intermolecular forces had gained general acceptance and he could write:

'The resistance of liquids and gases to external pressure tending to produce a diminution of volume, proves the existence of an internal force of an expansive or resisting character. On the other hand, the sudden diminution of volume, without the application of additional pressure externally, which occurs when a gas is compressed, at any temperature below the critical point, to the volume at which liquefaction begins, can scarcely be explained without assuming that a molecular force of great attractive power comes here into operation, and overcomes the resistance to diminution of volume, which commonly requires the application of external force . . .'

Van der Waals' equation

The surface shown in figure 4.4 is represented by the equation $pV = nRT$, the equation of state of an ideal gas. It would obviously be impossible to find a simple equation which would represent the complex p–V–T surface for a real substance, but there have been attempts to find equations to represent parts of the surface. For example, van der Waals, in 1879, proposed an equation of state to represent the behaviour of a substance in the gas-vapour-liquid region.

For gases at high pressure, or at temperatures near to the critical temperature or the boiling point, the assumptions of the simple kinetic theory are no longer valid for the following reasons.

1 The range of repulsive intermolecular forces is not infinitesimal compared with distances between molecules (so the effect of these forces must be considered).

2 The slightly longer range of attractive forces is not infinitesimal compared with distances between molecules (so the effect of these forces must be considered).

Q 4.10 Study question
State how van der Waals developed an equation of state more appropriate to the actual behaviour of gases than the equation $pV = nRT$. Account for the terms in the equation and compare the results predicted by van der Waals' equation with the experimental results for carbon dioxide in Andrews' experiment.■

4.2 Liquefaction of gases

Careful investigation of the behaviour of gases has shown that all gases can be liquefied if cooled enough.

Q 4.11 Self-assessment question
What is the essential condition necessary to liquefy a gas?■

The various methods for producing liquefied gases use three ways of cooling the gas.

1 Heat is removed from the gas. This is most commonly achieved by passing the gas through a heat exchanger containing an evaporating liquid. (Heat is removed in this way from your hand if a few drops of ether are poured on it.)

2 The gas is made to do external work by driving an engine, and this energy is provided at the expense of the molecular kinetic energy.

3 The gas is expanded rapidly, so that energy is required to separate the molecules and this energy is provided at the expense of the molecular kinetic energy (Joule-Kelvin cooling).

Q 4.12 Study question
Explain why a gas such as air cannot be liquefied by the application of pressure above room temperature and describe the liquefaction of air by the cascade process.■

Q 4.13 Study question
Explain why the cascade method cannot be used to liquefy hydrogen and describe one method for liquefying hydrogen.■

Helium is the substance with the lowest boiling point (about 4 K). At a temperature of 2.2 K the properties of liquid helium change dramatically to produce a liquid (helium II) with unique and unexpected properties. This eccentric material provides valuable clues about molecular energy and forces in normal matter.

Background reading
Near zero, by D.K.C. MacDonald, Heinemann, 1973.

Q 4.14 Study question
Briefly outline the unique properties of liquid helium and indicate what explanations have been given for them.■

4.3 Vapours

Consider now the transition from liquid to vapour. Molecules can leave a liquid and form a vapour if they have enough energy to overcome the intermolecular attractive forces in the liquid.

Evaporation

Q 4.15 Self-assessment question

(a) What evidence is there of forces of attraction between molecules in a liquid?

(b) What kinds of energy do molecules have in the liquid phase?

(c) What condition is necessary to enable a molecule to escape from the surface of a liquid?

(d) What can you predict about the effect of a rise in temperature on the rate at which molecules can escape from the surface of a liquid? Give reasons for your answer.■

A molecule, in the change from a liquid to a vapour phase, increases its potential energy at the expense of its kinetic energy. As a molecule in a vapour, it has less kinetic energy than it had when in the liquid because it has done work against the molecular attractive forces and so increased its molecular potential energy.

Q 4.16 Self-assessment question

How does the kinetic theory explain what may happen to the temperature of a liquid which is steadily evaporating?■

You can obtain evidence of this effect by pouring a drop of after-shave or acetone onto the back of your hand, or by showing how a film of water can be frozen under a beaker in which a liquid is evaporating rapidly.

Q 4.17 Self-assessment question

If evaporation is due to the escape of high speed molecules whose energy is sufficient to enable them to overcome intermolecular attraction forces, can evaporation take place (i) from solids, (ii) at all temperatures? Explain your answer. What evidence can you suggest to support it?■

We are very much aware of the constant evaporation taking place from liquids like petrol and methylated spirits: volatile liquids (as they are called). More surprisingly, a liquid like mercury, which is hardly volatile, is constantly evaporating and the poisonous vapour can constitute a health hazard.

When a substance changes from solid to liquid, or from liquid to vapour, energy must be supplied to break the molecular bonds. When a liquid is formed only a proportion of the molecular bonds are broken, so that in a liquid groups of molecules remain bonded together. The groups are not fixed relative to each other so the liquid loses its rigidity and can flow. (We say a liquid has short-range order, in contrast to long-range order in solids.) Once a liquid has been formed from a solid, the proportion of broken bonds remains constant, on average. However, when a liquid evaporates all the remaining bonds must be broken.

When a liquid evaporates, expansion occurs (and for most substances expansion also occurs on melting). Some energy must be supplied to do work against the external pressure (e.g. to push back the atmosphere). However, the energy required to do external work is usually only a very small proportion of the total energy required, and most of the energy supplied is used in separating the molecules from each other.

Figure 4.8 shows the variation in potential energy with separation between two molecules. The change in separation due to vibration of the molecules is indicated for a particular temperature T. At A and A', the vibrating molecule has maximum potential energy and zero kinetic energy.

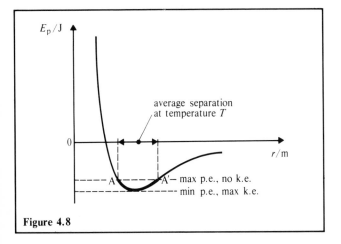

Figure 4.8

Q **4.18 Self-assessment question**
  (a) For water, the specific latent heats of fusion and vaporisation are 333 kJ kg^{-1} and 2260 kJ kg^{-1} respectively. Suggest a reason for this difference.
(b) Use figure 4.8 to explain why the latent heat of vaporisation of water has different values at 50 °C and 100 °C.
(c) Estimate the energy needed to enable one water molecule to escape, (if the molar mass of water is 0.018 kg mol^{-1}).■

Vapour saturating a space
Look back to figures 4.3 and 4.5 and consider the liquid–vapour region. Notice that, between A and B, vapour and liquid phases exist in equilibrium. The volume can have different values, but the pressure remains constant and its value for a particular vapour depends only on the temperature. This pressure is that exerted by a vapour in dynamic equilibrium with its liquid and is called the *saturated vapour pressure*.

Q **4.19 Development question***
  Figure 4.9 illustrates what may be observed when several small quantities of a volatile liquid, like ether, are introduced successively into the bottom of a mercury barometer tube. Explain the effects produced, in the sequence (a) to (d), using the terms *dynamic equilibrium* and *saturated vapour*.■

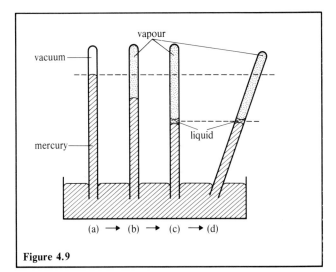

Figure 4.9

Q 4.20 Self-assessment question

The rate at which molecules leave a liquid depends on the average kinetic energy of the molecules. The rate at which molecules return to a liquid depends on the density of the vapour. Use these, and any other relevant facts, to explain how the saturated vapour pressure (s.v.p.) changes when the temperature is raised.■

Q 4.21 Development question*

(a) Explain why the pressure which a saturated vapour exerts does not depend on the volume of the container or the presence of another gas.

Hint. Think what happens to the dynamic equilibrium at the liquid surface when the volume of the container changes.

(b) Describe what happens when the space containing a saturated vapour is cooled without changing its volume. What change will occur in the pressure exerted by a saturated vapour if the temperature falls?

(c) A volume containing a saturated vapour and a small quantity of liquid is expanded steadily. Sketch a graph of the way in which the pressure changes as the volume increases.■

Q 4.22 Self-assessment question

Comment on the following statements.

(a) Carbon dioxide cylinders contain liquefied gas.

(b) The amount of carbon dioxide in a cylinder cannot be ascertained by means of a pressure gauge.■

Boiling

This occurs when bubbles of vapour form throughout a liquid. These bubbles begin as tiny air bubbles, growing rapidly as the liquid evaporates into them until the pressure of the air is insignificant compared to the pressure exerted by the vapour. If they exist long enough to rise and escape, the pressure inside the bubbles must equal the external pressure acting on them.

Q 4.23 Self-assessment question

What can you say about the saturated vapour pressure if the liquid is boiling? Predict what will happen to the boiling point if the external pressure is reduced. Give a reason for your answer.■

A liquid has many boiling points, since changing the external pressure will affect the temperature at which the liquid boils. However, we can speak of a normal boiling point as the temperature at which the liquid boils under a normal or standard atmospheric pressure.

Q 4.24 Self-assessment question

A pressure-cooker is fitted with a valve which can be loaded with a weight so that it opens when the pressure inside the cooker is twice the atmospheric pressure. 200 cm³ of water are put in the cooker with the food to be cooked, and the lid is put on before heating.

(a) Suggest reasons why (i) the valve must be kept open for 2 minutes before being loaded with the weight, (ii) only a small amount of water is required, (iii) the cooking time is very much less than that required when cooking in water boiling at normal atmospheric pressure.

(b) Estimate the approximate cooking temperature from the data given.

Temperature θ/°C	100	110	120	130
s.v.p. of water p/10^5 Pa	1.01	1.43	1.98	2.70

■

If a bubble of vapour is formed inside a liquid (figure 4.10), the pressure of the saturated vapour inside it must balance the pressure from outside. This includes the atmospheric pressure p_1 and the hydrostatic pressure p_2 due to the height of liquid above the bubble. Also, because surface tension forces act in the liquid surface trying to shrink a bubble, the pressure inside a bubble must exceed the pressure in the surrounding liquid by a pressure $p_3 = 2\gamma/r$, where r is the bubble radius and γ is the surface tension of the liquid. The pressure p_3 is only significant if the radius of the bubble is small.

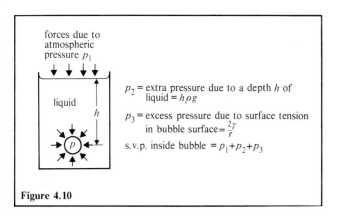

forces due to atmospheric pressure p_1

liquid

h

p

p_2 = extra pressure due to a depth h of liquid = $h\rho g$

p_3 = excess pressure due to surface tension in bubble surface = $\frac{2\gamma}{r}$

s.v.p. inside bubble = $p_1 + p_2 + p_3$

Figure 4.10

Q 4.25 Self-assessment question
If a liquid is being heated in a very tall container, suggest why the temperature at the bottom of the container can be higher than the normal boiling point before the liquid boils. ∎

Q 4.26 Self-assessment question
Show that for a bubble of vapour of a hundred molecular diameters to exist inside a liquid of surface tension 2.5×10^{-2} N m^{-1}, the vapour must exert a pressure of about fifty atmospheres (assume a molecular diameter is 2×10^{-10} m). ∎

Q 4.27 Self-assessment question
If *pure* water is heated *gently* in a *round-bottomed* flask, the temperature may rise above 100 °C without boiling occurring. Explain this, commenting on the significance of the words in italics. Suggest what might happen if the flask was made to vibrate or the external pressure acting on the water was rapidly reduced. ∎

Q 4.28 Self-assessment question
A sealed flask contains water and air saturated with water vapour at 20 °C and 100 kPa total pressure. Calculate the pressure in the vessel if it is heated to 100 °C without expanding. Assume the s.v.p. of water at 20 °C is 2.2 kPa and atmospheric pressure is 100 kPa. Would the water boil under these circumstances? Why? ∎

E Experiment TP6
Variation of s.v.p. of water with temperature
The boiling point of water is measured under different pressures and the results used to plot a graph of the variation of s.v.p. with temperature.

If the p–V–T surface for water is projected in two dimensions to give a p–T curve, the result is as shown in figure 4.11. The vaporisation curve starts at the triple point and ends at the critical point; the graph obtained in experiment TP6, of s.v.p. against temperature, is part of this curve.

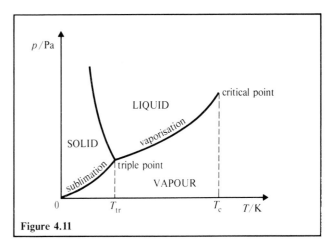

Figure 4.11

SYLLABUS EXTENSION

Clouds

Clouds are formed when damp air at the earth's surface rises into regions of lower pressure high in the atmosphere.

Q 4.29 Self-assessment question
Why does the air become saturated with water vapour as it rises?■

It is not always realised that the tracking of radioactive radiation in a cloud chamber by C.T.R. Wilson developed from his study of clouds and Scottish mists! He found that, in dust-free air, condensation into droplets did not occur when the vapour pressure reached saturation point. Often the vapour pressure was 1.25 times the s.v.p. before drops formed.

Figure 4.12 indicates the region (sphere of influence) around a molecule in which short range intermolecular attractive forces are significant.

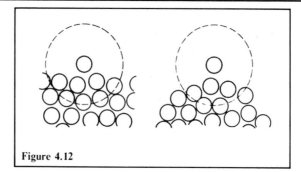

Figure 4.12

Q 4.30 Study question
(a) Use figure 4.12 to explain why evaporation occurs more easily from a convex than a flat surface.
(b) Hence explain why it is very difficult for a vapour to condense into tiny drops without a high degree of supersaturation.
(c) Why do drops form at all?■

Wilson also found that condensation occurs without much supersaturation if the air has been ionised. The ions act as centres of condensation and drops form rapidly around these charges. By the rapid expansion of a saturated vapour, Wilson produced heavy condensation on ions and photographed the trails of ionised drops.

Q 4.31 Self-assessment question
(a) What word is appropriate to describe the rapid expansion of vapour in a Wilson cloud chamber, and what kind of temperature change is produced?
(b) Another type of cloud chamber, called a diffusion cloud chamber or a continuous cloud chamber, was referred to in the Unit *Structure of matter*. Solid carbon dioxide is placed under a thermally conducting plate below the cloud chamber which contains saturated vapour. Explain how the cloud chamber works, saying what is 'diffusing' and why it acts 'continuously'.
(c) Before using the cloud chamber, the transparent plastic top is rubbed with a duster. Explain why.■

Q 4.32 Self-assessment question
Ionisation also assists the formation of bubbles of vapour in a liquid and this is utilised to produce ionisation tracks in superheated liquid in a bubble chamber.
(a) At what temperature is the liquid maintained?
(b) What is the effect of rapidly reducing the pressure inside the liquid?
(c) Why should the tracks in a bubble chamber be more continuous than in a cloud chamber?■

Questions on objectives

1 Explain what is meant by a saturated vapour.

(objective 1)

2 (a) In figure 4.13 the tube above the mercury meniscus B contains only a liquid and its saturated vapour, and it is maintained at a constant temperature of 50 °C. The atmospheric pressure is 760 mmHg and the vertical distance AB is about 50 mm. Describe what will happen if more mercury is poured in at A and use the kinetic theory to explain your prediction. Is the normal boiling point of the liquid above or below 50 °C? Explain.
(b) State, and explain in simple kinetic theory terms, what happens if the temperature of the bath is increased above 50 °C.

(objectives 2 and 3)

3 Sketch pressure against temperature graphs between 0 °C and 100 °C for (i) an ideal gas, (ii) saturated water vapour and (iii) a mixture of gas and saturated water vapour.

(objective 3)

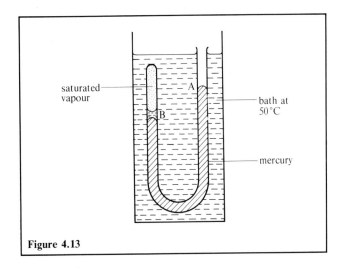

saturated vapour

A

B

bath at 50 °C

mercury

Figure 4.13

4 Indicate to what extent hydrogen, nitrogen and carbon dioxide can be expected to behave like an ideal gas in the region of standard temperature at pressures of (i) 10^5 Pa (one atmosphere) and (ii) 5×10^6 Pa. Give reasons for your answer.

(objective 4)

5 Sketch p–V isothermals for the gas–liquid states and indicate the region in which $pV = nRT$ applies. Indicate the state of the substance in the various regions of the p–V diagram. Mark and explain the critical isothermal.

(objectives 2 and 4)

6 Describe, with the aid of a diagram, an experiment to determine the saturated vapour pressure of water in the temperature range 50 °C to 100 °C.

(objective 5)

7 A mixture of air and saturated water vapour is contained in a closed vessel under a pressure of 1210 mmHg and at a temperature of 75 °C. Calculate the pressure
(a) if the temperature is reduced to 30 °C, and
(b) if the volume is then halved, at the new temperature.
(s.v.p. water at 75 °C = 289 mmHg, s.v.p. water at 30 °C = 32 mmHg.)

(objective 6)

Chapter 5

Thermal conduction

Aim

The aim of this chapter is to enable you to understand the conduction of heat through good and bad conductors. To achieve this, you will study experimental methods to determine thermal conductivity, develop a theory to explain the mechanism of conduction and solve problems related to the practical application of the topic.

Chapter

5

Study time: 1½ weeks

Objectives

When you have completed the work in this chapter you should be able to:

1 Use the following scientific terms correctly: thermal conduction, steady state.

2 Define and use the following scientific terms and recall their standard symbols and units: temperature gradient, thermal conductivity.

3 Describe and explain, with the aid of suitable graphs, the temperature distribution along a lagged bar and an unlagged bar, the ends of which are kept at different temperatures.

4 Explain the factors which determine the rate of flow of thermal energy through a material.

5 Explain the principles of the measurement of thermal conductivity.

6 Describe experiments to determine the thermal conductivities of solids of high or low conductivity (i.e. good and poor conductors) and show how the result is obtained from the measurements.

7 Solve problems involving thermal conductivity.

8 EXTENSION
Compare and contrast thermal conduction and electrical conduction in metals.

9 EXTENSION
Describe qualitatively the mechanisms of thermal conduction in metals and non-metals.

Experiments in chapter 5

There are no experiments in this chapter.

References

Adkins	Chapter 2
Duncan MM	Chapter 4
Hands	Chapter 7
Millar	Chapter 9
Nelkon	Chapter 14
Whelan	Chapter 29

5.1 The transfer of heat

Energy can be transferred from one body to another, or from one part of a body to another part, in two ways, which we call heat and work. (Work is not confined to mechanical work, but also includes, for example, electrical work.) In this chapter we are concerned only with heat.

The fact that a hot body falls in temperature is evidence of the fact that energy is transferred to the surroundings. There are three ways by which this takes place.

Q 5.1 Study question
Describe and distinguish between the three methods of heat transfer.■

The foundation of the study of conduction was laid by the French mathematician and physicist Fourier (1768-1830), who by experiment and intuition devised a mathematical method for solving problems. It is interesting to note that it was this work which inspired Ohm to apply similar ideas to the conduction of electricity through metals, which led to the formulation of Ohm's law. This parallel between thermal and electrical conduction will be brought out in this chapter.

Q 5.2 Self-assessment question
Some electrical devices can become too hot when in operation, and then they do not function properly. This can be avoided by fastening the device (for example, a power transistor) in *good thermal contact* with a *heat sink,* such as a piece of aluminium sheet with aluminium fins as shown in figure 5.1.
(a) Suggest a reason why this is called a heat sink.
(b) What does good thermal contact mean?
(c) Explain in detail how the heat is carried away from

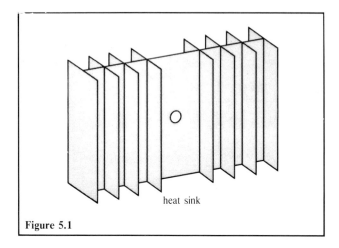

heat sink

Figure 5.1

the electrical device to the air *outside* the apparatus.
(d) Why is the heat sink made with fins?
(e) Discuss whether the heat sink should be placed vertically (as in figure 5.1) or horizontally.
(f) A manufacturer writes, 'If the centre of the aluminium rises 30 °C above the surroundings, then the rate of heat dissipation is 12.5 watt'. Explain what this statement means, saying what is meant by a 'watt'.
(g) The manufacturer also provides figures for 15 °C, 45 °C and 60 °C temperature rise:

Temperature rise / °C	0	15	30	45	60
Rate of heat loss / watts	0	6.0	12.5	20.0	29.0

Plot on a graph all five points provided by these figures, plotting temperature rise along the x-axis and the rate of heat loss up the y-axis. Draw the graph.
(h) What does the graph show about the way in which rate of heat loss varies with temperature rise?■

5.2 Thermal conduction

Temperature gradient
Conduction is the transfer of energy due to a difference in temperature between adjacent parts of an object or material.

Q 5.3 Study question*
A solid bar (figure 5.2a) is heated at one end. The temperature of the bar at different points along its length rises until, after a time, the temperature at any point, such as P, is constant.
(a) Why does the temperature at a point eventually attain a steady value?
(b) The graph in figure 5.2b shows the way in which the temperature along the bar varies with distance x when conditions are steady and the bar is lagged. Figure 5.2c shows the temperature distribution if the bar is unlagged. Comment on the features of the graphs, and explain why each graph has this particular form.
(c) Explain, with the aid of these graphs, what is meant by *temperature gradient*. How would you obtain the value of the temperature gradient for the point P (i) for the lagged bar, and (ii) for the unlagged bar.
(d) For a uniform bar, what is the relationship between the temperature gradient and the rate of flow of heat?
(e) For a fixed temperature gradient, how does the rate of heat flow depend on the area of cross-section of the bar?■

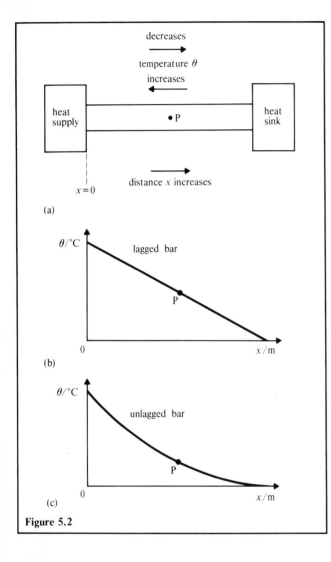

(a)

(b)

(c)

Figure 5.2

Thermal conductivity

Thermal conductivity is a measure of how well a material will conduct heat. It also provides a way of comparing the rates of flow of heat in different materials under the same conditions.

Consider a thin disc of the material, such as that shown in figure 5.3, of thickness Δx and uniform cross-sectional area A. Suppose that when there is a temperature difference $\Delta\theta$ across the disc a quantity of heat ΔQ flows through the disc in a time Δt. Experiments show that the rate of flow of heat through the disc is

1 proportional to the temperature gradient, for fixed cross-sectional area

$$\frac{\Delta Q}{\Delta t} \propto \frac{\Delta\theta}{\Delta x}$$

2 proportional to the cross-sectional area, for fixed temperature gradient

$$\frac{\Delta Q}{\Delta t} \propto A$$

Thus the rate of flow of heat is given by the expression

$$\frac{\Delta Q}{\Delta t} \propto A \frac{\Delta\theta}{\Delta x}$$

$$\text{or } \frac{\Delta Q}{\Delta t} = -\lambda A \frac{\Delta\theta}{\Delta x}$$

where λ is a constant of proportionality, called the thermal conductivity. (Some text books use the symbol k for thermal conductivity.)

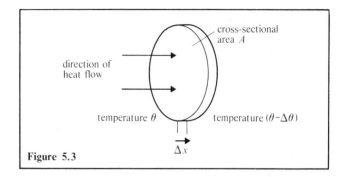

Figure 5.3

Note: The negative sign is included because heat flows from a region of high to low temperature (i.e. x increases as θ decreases). The temperature gradient $d\theta/dx$ is negative. Insertion of the negative sign ensures that dQ/dt and λ will be positive.

If we take the limiting case of this expression, when $\Delta x \to 0$, so that we are considering a *cross-section*, then

$$\frac{dQ}{dt} = -\lambda A \frac{d\theta}{dx}$$

This is the equation which defines *thermal conductivity* – the justification for it is based on experimental evidence.

Q **5.4 Self-assessment question**
(a) Explain in words the meaning of thermal conductivity.
(b) Show that the unit of thermal conductivity is the watt per metre kelvin, $W\ m^{-1}\ K^{-1}$. ■

Theories of the mechanism of thermal conduction indicate that thermal conductivity should be constant over a wide range of temperature gradients, should not depend upon the cross-sectional area of the specimen and should be the same for both steady and non-steady conditions. These results are confirmed by experiment.

However, at very low temperatures near absolute zero, the conductivity is dependent upon cross-sectional area (for many materials $\lambda \propto \sqrt{A}$ as the temperature tends to absolute zero). For pure metals the thermal conductivity rises slightly as the temperature is reduced, except at very low temperatures when (as for all materials) it then tends to zero.

Parallel flow

In the case of a perfectly insulated bar, the lines of heat flow (that is, lines which indicate the direction in which the heat is being conducted) are parallel. The bar illustrated in figure 5.4 is of length x and cross-sectional area A. Its opposite ends are maintained at temperatures θ_1 and θ_2, where $\theta_1 > \theta_2$. In this case the temperature gradient is the same at every cross-section. Thus

$$\frac{\mathrm{d}\theta}{\mathrm{d}x} = \frac{(\theta_2 - \theta_1)}{x} = -\frac{(\theta_1 - \theta_2)}{x}$$

and the defining equation for λ can be expressed as

$$\frac{Q}{t} = \lambda A \frac{(\theta_1 - \theta_2)}{x}$$

where Q is the heat that flows through any section in a time t. (This expression is sometimes referred to as Fourier's heat flow equation.)

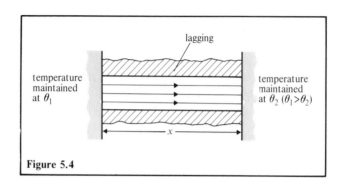

Figure 5.4

Q 5.5 Self-assessment question

When the rate of heat flow per unit area of a sheet of insulating material, thickness 5.00 mm, is 15 kW m^{-2}, the temperature drop across the slab is 100 K. Calculate the thermal conductivity of the material.∎

Q 5.6 Self-assessment question

(a) A room has windows made of glass 4.0 mm thick with a total surface area of 5.0 m². The thermal conductivity of glass is 0.8 W m^{-1} K^{-1}. If the temperature of the room is 19 °C and the temperature outside is 1 °C, estimate the rate of loss of heat by conduction through the glass.

(b) How many 3 kW electric fires would be needed to compensate for this loss and keep the temperature of the room constant?

(c) Most rooms in a house can be heated adequately by one 3 kW fire. What assumptions have been made in part (a), and why is the estimated value of the rate of heat loss much too high?

(d) How can heat loss through the windows of a room be reduced?∎

Q 5.7 Self-assessment question

(a) Figure 5.5 represents part of a boiler made of steel plates 6.0 mm thick. The area exposed to the furnace is 8.0 m². When steady conditions have been attained, steam is produced at a rate of 0.32 kg s^{-1}. The thermal conductivity of steel is 48 W m^{-1} K^{-1}, and the specific latent heat of vaporisation of water is 2.3×10^6 J kg^{-1}. Calculate the temperature drop across the boiler plates.

(b) In practice, why must the temperature difference between the flame and the water be higher than that calculated for the boiler plates if steam is to be produced at the rate given above.∎

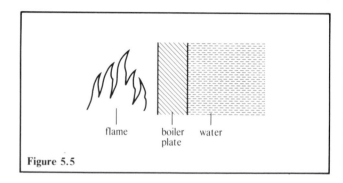

Figure 5.5

Q 5.8 Self-assessment question

When hard water is heated in an electric kettle, scale is deposited on the element of the kettle and on the inside walls. Explain the effect of this deposit on the time the kettle takes to boil.∎

EXTENSION

Problems involving integration

Q 5.9 Study question*

The ice on a pond is 2.0 cm thick and the temperature of the air above it is $-10\,°C$. Find the time that will elapse before the thickness of the ice increases to 3 cm. State the assumptions made in your calculation.

($\lambda_{ice} = 2.0\ W\ m^{-1}\ K^{-1}$, specific latent heat of fusion of ice $= 3.3 \times 10^5\ J\ kg^{-1}$, density of ice $= 0.9 \times 10^3\ kg\ m^{-3}$.)■

Q 5.10 Study question*

A metal pipe of outer radius 10 mm carries steam at 100 °C. It is insulated by a close-fitting sleeve of expanded polystyrene 15 mm thick.
(a) Calculate the rate of loss of heat from a 10 m length of pipe if the surrounding air is at 20 °C.
(b) At what rate would steam condense in this length of pipe as a result of the heat loss?

($\lambda_{polystyrene} = 4.0 \times 10^{-2}\ W\ m^{-1}\ K^{-1}$, specific latent heat of vaporisation of water $= 2.26 \times 10^6\ J\ kg^{-1}$.)■

SYLLABUS EXTENSION

Analogy between thermal and electrical conduction

We can compare the rate of flow of heat in thermal conduction with the rate of flow of charge in electrical conduction. What must there be across a material in order for heat to flow? There must be a *temperature difference*.

Q 5.11 Development question

(a) What must be applied across a resistor in order for a current to pass through it?
(b) Show that the rate of flow of charge (i.e. the current) I through a resistor of length l and cross-sectional area A is given by

$$I = \frac{AV}{\rho l}$$

where ρ is the resistivity and V is the potential difference across the resistor.■

Rewriting this expression in terms of electrical conductivity σ,

$$I = \sigma A\ (V/l)$$

$$\frac{\text{rate of flow}}{\text{of charge}} = \frac{\text{electrical}}{\text{conductivity}} \times \frac{\text{cross-}}{\text{sectional}} \times \frac{\text{potential}}{\text{gradient}}$$
$$\text{area}$$

Compare this with Fourier's heat flow equation

$$\frac{Q}{t} = -\lambda A\ \frac{(\theta_1 - \theta_2)}{x}$$

$$\frac{\text{rate of flow}}{\text{of heat}} = \frac{\text{thermal}}{\text{conductivity}} \times \frac{\text{cross-}}{\text{sectional}} \times \frac{\text{temperature}}{\text{gradient}}$$
$$\text{area}$$

Q 5.12 Self-assessment question

By comparing the equations for rate of flow of heat and rate of flow of charge, relate the appropriate quantities.■

5.3 Measuring thermal conductivity

Who needs to know anyway? Well, mainly engineers, architects and geophysicists.

The usual way of measuring thermal conductivity is to supply heat, by electrical or steam heating, at a steady rate and measure the resultant temperature gradient, the apparatus being designed so that the rate of flow of heat can be easily measured. One of the simplest arrangements is to ensure that the flow of heat through the material is parallel. This is the case when the material is in the form of a cylinder which is well insulated. The method used will also depend upon the expected value of the thermal conductivity of the material.

For a *good conductor,* the problem is to achieve an appreciable temperature difference without having an excessive input of power.

For a *poor conductor,* the problem is to ensure that the rate of flow of heat through the material is sufficient to be accurately measured.

EXTENSION

Q 5.13 Study question

In what sort of situations might it be important to know the value of thermal conductivity. List a few examples of such situations. Where would a designer get the information? Where would it have come from in the first place?■

Q 5.14 Self-assessment question

(a) What sort of shape would be appropriate for a specimen of a good conductor?
(b) What sort of shape would be appropriate for a specimen of a poor conductor?
(c) Why would it be inappropriate to have the poor conductor in the form of a long bar?
(d) Why should the cross-sectional area of the poor conductor be large?■

An experiment which can be performed to illustrate the principle of the measurement of the thermal conductivity of a good conductor is one that was originally designed by Searle. This is usually carried out in the school laboratory with copper as the conductor. The thermal conductivity of a poor conductor can be obtained by an experiment which was designed by Lees.

Q 5.15 Study question

Make notes on a method of measuring the thermal conductivity of a good conductor. Include details of the apparatus, experimental procedure, the measurements that you would take and an explanation of how you would calculate the thermal conductivity.■

Q 5.16 Self-assessment question

The thermal conductivity of a metal is determined using a form of Searle's apparatus (figure 5.6). The heat is supplied by means of an electrical heater and the power input is 5.00 A at 10.0 V. The ammeter and voltmeter can be read to an accuracy of ±0.02 A and ±0.05 V respectively. The diameter of the bar is 5.00 cm and is measured by means of calipers to an accuracy of ±0.01 cm. The distance between the thermometers is 25.00 cm and is measured by means of a rule to an accuracy of ±0.05 cm. The readings on thermometers T_1 and T_2, when steady state conditions have been reached, are 48.0 °C and 32.0 °C respectively, measured to an accuracy of ±0.1 °C.

(a) Assuming that all the internal energy produced is conducted along the bar, use the data provided to obtain a value for the thermal conductivity of the material.
(b) Calculate the maximum percentage error in the following quantities:
(i) the diameter of the bar,
(ii) the distance between the thermometers,
(iii) the difference in temperature,
(iv) the rate of supply of electrical energy.
(c) Using the above results obtain a value for the maximum error in the calculated value of the thermal conductivity.
(d) Which measurement contributes most to this error? Suggest a way to improve it.■

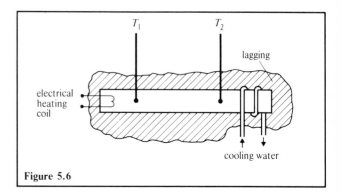

Figure 5.6

Q 5.17 Study question

Make notes on Lees' method of measuring the thermal conductivity of a poor conductor. Include details of the apparatus and experimental procedure, including an account of how the rate of flow of heat through the disc is measured. State the measurements that you would take and explain how you would calculate the thermal conductivity. ■

Q 5.18 Self-assessment question

Figure 5.7 shows a method of measuring the thermal conductivity λ_r of a sample of rock of thickness x_r. It makes use of a silica disc of known thermal conductivity λ_s and thickness x_s. When conditions are steady, the readings on the thermocouple thermometers T_1, T_2 and T_3 are θ_1, θ_2 and θ_3 respectively. Derive an expression for λ_r in terms of λ_s, x_r, x_s, θ_1, θ_2 and θ_3. ■

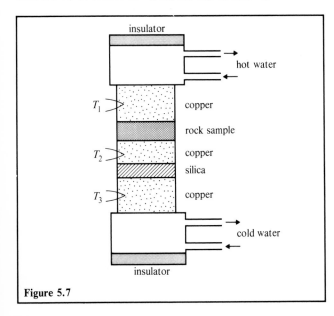

Figure 5.7

Q 5.19 Self-assessment question

Figure 5.8 shows a modified version of a Lees' disc experiment to determine the thermal conductivity of a poorly conducting material. Discs of the material under test are placed on either side of a heating element and two thick copper plates act as heat sinks. These are maintained at a constant temperature by circulating a cooling liquid through channels in the plates. The temperatures of the inner and outer surfaces of the material are measured by thermocouples. The rate at which energy is supplied is maintained constant until steady state conditions have been achieved.

Use the following experimental data to calculate the thermal conductivity of the material:

cross-sectional area of each disc = 4.13×10^2 cm^2,
thickness of each disc = 25.0 mm,
potential difference = 39.0 V,
current = 0.10 A,
temperature of inner surface = 21.2 °C,
temperature of outer surface = 14.4 °C. ■

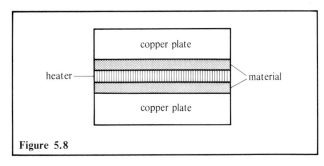

Figure 5.8

5.4 Reducing heat losses

Why should a building be insulated?

The function of a central heating system is to maintain the temperatures of the rooms of a building at particular values (for example, living rooms at 21 °C, 294 K, 70 °F) as heat is lost through walls, windows, roof, floor and doors. Heat must also be supplied to warm ventilation air (that is, fresh air which comes in to replace stale air).

Heat loss from a building can be minimised by insulating the roof, by double glazing, and by filling cavity walls with an insulating material such as urea formaldehyde foam. To illustrate this, we will consider the transfer of heat through a cavity wall (figure 5.9).

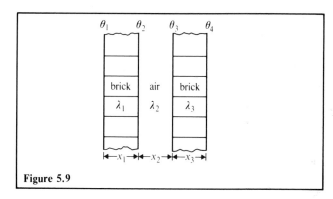

Figure 5.9

Assume that a steady state has been reached and that the lines of heat flow are parallel. The rates of flow of heat Q/t through each component of the cavity wall will be equal. Thus from Fourier's heat flow equation we have

$$\frac{Q}{t} = \lambda_1 A \frac{(\theta_1 - \theta_2)}{x_1} = \lambda_2 A \frac{(\theta_2 - \theta_3)}{x_2} = \lambda_3 A \frac{(\theta_3 - \theta_4)}{x_3}$$

From these equations any of the temperatures or the rate of flow of heat can be determined.

Q **5.20 Self-assessment question**
The wall of a building consists of a solid brick wall 25.0 cm thick with a plaster seal 2.5 cm thick on the inside. The inside and outside air temperatures are 25 °C (298 K) and 1 °C (274 K) respectively. Assume that there is a temperature drop of 3 K across the 'surface air' adjacent to the inside and outside walls, that steady state conditions have been attained, and that the lines of heat flow are parallel. Calculate
(a) the temperature at the junction between the brick and plaster,
(b) the temperature gradient across each component,
(c) the rate of flow of heat per unit area through the wall.
($\lambda_{\text{plaster}} = 0.60$ W m^{-1} K^{-1}, $\lambda_{\text{brick}} = 0.75$ W m^{-1} K^{-1}.)■

Thermal resistance

Heating engineers are usually concerned with the rate of flow of heat through composite structures, such as a cavity wall (figure 5.9), and find it more convenient to have an expression for the rate of flow of heat per unit area, Φ, in terms of θ_1 and θ_4 (the surface temperatures of the sides of the structure).

For conduction through the thickness x_1 we have

$$\frac{Q}{t} = \lambda_1 A \frac{(\theta_1 - \theta_2)}{x_1}$$

Rearranging, $(\theta_1 - \theta_2) = Qx_1/tA\lambda_1$.
Let $R_1 = x_1/\lambda_1$, and $\Phi = Q/tA$, then $(\theta_1 - \theta_2) = \Phi R_1$.
Similarly, $(\theta_2 - \theta_3) = \Phi R_2$ and $(\theta_3 - \theta_4) = \Phi R_3$, where $R_2 = x_2/\lambda_2$ and $R_3 = x_3/\lambda_3$. Thus

$$(\theta_1 - \theta_4) = \Phi(R_1 + R_2 + R_3)$$

Compare this with the expression for the rate of flow of charge through three resistors in series,

$$V = I(R_1 + R_2 + R_3)$$

Hence, by analogy, x/λ is called the thermal resistance of the material. The rate of flow of heat per unit area, Φ, is given by

$$\Phi = \frac{\text{total temperature difference}}{\text{total thermal resistance}}$$

Q **5.21 Self-assessment question**
What is the unit of thermal resistance?■

Q **5.22 Self-assessment question**
To illustrate the effect of high thermal resistance, compare the rate of flow of heat per unit area through a solid brick wall with that through a cavity wall which is filled with insulating foam, using the information given below. Assume steady state conditions, parallel flow and that the inside and outside surface temperatures are 21 °C (294 K) and 1 °C (274 K) respectively.
$\lambda_{\text{brick}} = 0.80$ W m^{-1} K^{-1},
$\lambda_{\text{foam}} = 0.03$ W m^{-1} K^{-1},
solid brick wall: 200 mm thick,
cavity wall: bricks 2×100 mm thick, with a 50 mm cavity.■

In deriving and using the equations for heat flow through a composite structure, the temperatures θ_1 and θ_4 were assumed to be the actual surface temperatures at opposite sides of the structure. In practice, the measured temperatures are the bulk air temperatures in the vicinity of the sides of the structure. These will not be equal to the surface temperatures, due to the presence of layers of semi-stagnant air in contact with the surfaces. To allow for this, *surface resistances* are introduced as if the layers of air were part of the structure.

Q **5.23 Self-assessment question**
Suppose the surface resistances for the inside and outside of the wall in question 5.22 are 0.10 W^{-1} m^2 K and 0.05 W^{-1} m^2 K respectively. How will this affect the rate of flow of heat through the solid brick wall?■

U-values

Another quantity that gives us information about the conduction of heat through a material is its *thermal transmittance* or *U*-value. This is the rate of flow of heat through unit area of material when the temperature difference between opposite faces is 1 K.

Q 5.24 Self-assessment question
(a) What is the unit of thermal transmittance?
(b) What is the relationship between the thermal resistance and the *U*-value of a material?■

The *U*-value of a composite structure in which the components have thermal resistances of R_1, R_2 and R_3 is given by

$$U = \frac{1}{R_1 + R_2 + R_3}$$

The rate of flow of heat through a surface is given by

$$\frac{Q}{t} = UA\,(\theta_1 - \theta_2)$$

Q 5.25 Self-assessment question
(a) Use the data provided to calculate the *U*-value of the wall shown in figure 5.10.
$\lambda_{\text{brick}} = 0.84 \text{ W m}^{-1} \text{ K}^{-1}$,
$\lambda_{\text{concrete}} = 0.23 \text{ W m}^{-1} \text{ K}^{-1}$,
$\lambda_{\text{plaster}} = 0.18 \text{ W m}^{-1} \text{ K}^{-1}$,

thermal resistance of unventilated airspace, $R_{\text{cav}} = 0.18 \text{ W}^{-1} \text{ m}^2 \text{ K}$,
internal surface resistance, $R_{\text{si}} = 0.12 \text{ W}^{-1} \text{ m}^2 \text{ K}$,
external surface resistance, $R_{\text{so}} = 0.05 \text{ W}^{-1} \text{ m}^2 \text{ K}$.
(b) Calculate the effect of filling the cavity with polyurethane foam ($\lambda_{\text{foam}} = 0.03 \text{ W m}^{-1} \text{ K}^{-1}$).
(c) If the above structure forms an external wall of a room of height 2.20 m and width 3.50 m, compare the rates of loss of heat for the unfilled and filled cavity. The inside and outside air temperatures are 21.0 °C and 0.0 °C respectively.■

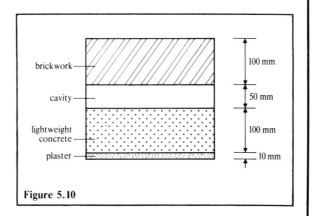

Figure 5.10

C Computer program
HEATER
This program contains a detailed model of the way a domestic building loses heat, and makes use of a large amount of data to calculate the yearly heat loss and to compute the costs of heating the building using the normally available fuels.

5.5 Mechanism of conduction

There are two principal mechanisms by which heat is conducted through a material: one involves the vibration of atoms, the other the movement of electrons.

When a solid is heated, the atoms near the source will vibrate more violently about their equilibrium positions in the lattice than their less energetic neighbours. Atoms are held in position in the solid by forces which connect them to neighbouring atoms (this is known as interatomic bonding). The neighbouring atoms will be affected by the increased motion. They will vibrate more vigorously and, in turn, affect other atoms. A disturbance will travel through the material and energy is transferred.

Heat is conducted in all solids by lattice vibration, but for metals and alloys there is another mechanism which predominates.

The observation that good conductors of electricity are also good conductors of heat (the experimental work of Wiedemann and Franz showed that the ratio of the thermal and electrical conductivities is the same for all metals at the same temperature) led scientists to the conclusion that the same agent is responsible for the transfer of heat and the transfer of charge.

Q 5.26 Self-assessment question
What other type of energy is transmitted by lattice vibration?■

Q 5.27 Self-assessment question
What is the agent responsible for the transfer of heat by conduction in metals?■

We can picture the interior of a conductor as a three-dimensional lattice of atoms with free electrons moving among the atoms and colliding frequently with them. The atoms vibrate about their equilibrium positions. The electrons move among them, with mean energy which is determined by the absolute temperature of the conductor. (On this model the electrons can be considered to behave like gas molecules. The ideas developed in chapter 3 on the kinetic theory of gases can be used, and each electron has a thermal energy of $\frac{3}{2}kT$.)

Electrical conduction in metals may be explained on this model as the drifting of free electrons under the influence of an electric field or potential gradient. How can this model explain the conduction of heat in metals?

When a temperature gradient is set up along a metal bar, since the mean energy of the electrons depends on the temperature, electrons at the hotter end will have more energy than those at the cooler end. The electrons diffuse through the metal from the hotter end to the cooler end and transfer energy.

Q 5.28 Study question
Compare and contrast the mechanisms by which heat is conducted through a metal and a gas.■

The free electron theory which was developed by Drude at the beginning of this century explained successfully electrical and thermal conduction and agreed with the empirical law of Wiedemann, Franz and Lorenz, namely

$$\frac{\lambda}{\sigma} \propto T$$

where T is the absolute temperature.

Background reading
For a detailed account of the theory read Wenham, chapter 44.

Questions on objectives

1 Which of the following is the unit of thermal conductivity?

A $J \, kg^{-1} \, K^{-1}$ D $W^{-1} \, m \, K^{-1}$
B $W \, m \, K^{-1}$ E $J \, m^{-1} \, K^{-1}$
C $W \, m^{-1} \, K^{-1}$

(objective 2)

2 Explain the meaning of the underlined word/s in the following statement.
'Heat is transported through the earth's crust by <u>thermal conduction</u> and the rate of flow of heat per unit cross-sectional area is equal to the product of the <u>temperature gradient</u> and the <u>thermal conductivity</u>.'

(objectives 1 and 2)

3 The ends of a straight uniform metal rod are maintained at 100 °C and 20 °C, the temperature of the surroundings being below 20 °C.
(a) Sketch graphs to show the variation of the temperature of the rod along its length when the surface is (i) lagged and (ii) unlagged.
(b) Explain the features of each graph.

(objective 3)

4 Figure 5.11 represents, in outline, Searle's apparatus which can be used to determine the thermal conductivity of a good conductor.
(a) Explain how the rate of heat flow is measured.
(b) State what measurements you would take and, using the appropriate symbols for these quantities, derive an expression from which the thermal conductivity could be calculated.
(c) Why is a thick bar used in this determination?
(d) Why is it necessary to insulate the bar?
(e) Why is it necessary to wait for some time before taking temperature readings?

(f) Explain the reason why either mercury or glycerine is placed in the holes which contain the thermometers T_1 and T_2.

(objectives 5 and 6)

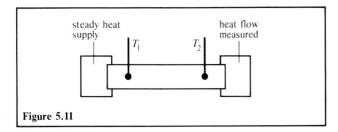

Figure 5.11

5 Figure 5.12 represents, in outline, Lees' disc apparatus which can be used to determine the thermal conductivity of a poor conductor.
(a) Explain how the rate of heat flow through the disc is measured.
(b) State what measurements you would take and, using the appropriate symbols for the quantities, derive an expression from which the thermal conductivity could be calculated.
(c) Why is a thin disc of the material used in this determination?
(d) Why must the adjoining surfaces of C, B and D be clean and flat and the sides of C and B be polished?

(objectives 5 and 6)

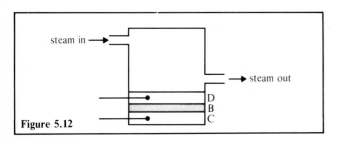

Figure 5.12

6 Two metal bars of the same cross-sectional area are 0.4 m and 0.5 m long and have thermal conductivities 80 and 25 W m^{-1} K^{-1} respectively. They are welded together end to end, and the outer end of the first bar is at 373 K when the outer end of the second bar is at 293 K. Assuming that no heat leaves the sides of the bar, what is the temperature of the welded joint?

(objective 7)

7 It has been suggested that geothermal energy (i.e. energy from hot rocks) might be used in the U.K. To locate rocks which are hot enough to be useful at a reasonable depth, information is needed about how temperature increases with depth at various places. Boring holes is too expensive (about £1 million for a 4 km deep hole), so the problem must be approached by calculation, using data from shallow bore-holes.
(a) Write down the equation relating the rate of heat flow from within the earth over a given area to the temperature gradient.
(b) Explain why it is not necessary to consider heat losses.
(c) Data from a certain bore-hole are given in table 5.1. Are these data consistent with a constant heat flow at different depths? If so, what is it? If not, explain.
(d) It is thought that below 225 m the value of the thermal conductivity is about the same down to 600 m, and below that is about 1.9 W m^{-1} K^{-1}. Estimate the temperature of the rock at a depth of 4.0 km.
(e) Given that the cost of drilling is largely unaffected by the type of rock, what two factors should you look for if you are trying to find a good place to drill a bore-hole up to 4 km deep as a source of geothermal energy?
(f) Suggest reasons why measurements of the top 40 m are ignored.

(objective 7)

Table 5.1

Depth x/m	Temperature T/K	Thermal conductivity λ/W m^{-1} K^{-1}
40	298.5 ⎱	
85	299.7 ⎰ stratum 1	2.7
225	302.6	stratum 2 3.5

8 EXTENSION
Discuss the analogy between the flow of heat through a perfectly lagged conductor of uniform cross-sectional area and the flow of charge through a resistor.

(objective 8)

9 EXTENSION
Table 5.2 lists the values of thermal conductivity and electrical conductivity for some elements. All values are at 273 K.
(a) The Wiedemann-Franz law states that the ratio λ/σ is the same for all metals at a given temperature. To what extent do the values given support this law?
(b) The relationship applies for metals but not for non-metals. Compare and contrast the conduction processes for heat and electricity in metals.
(c) Explain the process by which heat is conducted in electrical insulators and semiconductors.

(objective 9)

Table 5.2

Element	λ/10^2 W m^{-1} K^{-1}	σ/10^7 Ω^{-1} m^{-1}
aluminium	2.36	4.1
copper	4.03	6.5
iron	0.84	1.1
lead	0.36	0.52
silver	4.28	6.8

Chapter

Thermal radiation

Aim

The aim of this chapter is to enable you to acquire an understanding of thermal radiation. To achieve this you will study ways in which radiation can be detected, the concept of black body radiation and how the energy in the spectrum of black body radiation depends upon wavelength and temperature.

Solar furnace in the Pyrenees

Chapter

6

Study time: 1 week

Objectives

When you have completed the work in this chapter you should be able to:

1 Use correctly the following scientific terms: black body, black body radiation.

2 Define and use correctly the following scientific terms and recall their standard symbols and units (where appropriate):
Stefan-Boltzmann constant, total radiant exitance, total emissivity, total absorptance, spectral radiant exitance, spectral emissivity, spectral absorptance.

3 Describe the principles of the thermopile.

4 State and explain what is meant by Prévost's theory of exchanges.

5 (a) Explain what is meant by a black body and by black body radiation.
(b) Describe and explain how an almost perfect black body can be realised in practice.

6 State Stefan's law of black body radiation.

7 (a) Sketch curves to show how the energy radiated from a black body varies with wavelength at various temperatures.
(b) Describe and explain the features of these curves.

8 State and explain Wien's displacement law.

9 Discuss how the power radiated and absorbed by a surface depends upon its nature.

10 Solve problems on thermal radiation involving Prévost's theory of exchanges, Stefan's law and Wien's displacement law.

11 EXTENSION
Explain the principles of (a) a total radiation pyrometer, (b) an optical pyrometer and (c) a bolometer.

12 EXTENSION
Outline how the distribution of energy in the spectrum of a black body can be investigated experimentally.

13 Discuss qualitatively how classical physics failed to account for black body radiation, and the theory put forward by Planck.

Experiment in chapter 6
TP7 Heat loss of a filament lamp
(1 hour)

References

Adkins	Chapter 6
Duncan FWA	Chapter 8
Hands	Chapter 8
Millar	Chapter 29
Nelkon	Chapter 14
Whelan	Chapter 30

6.1 Detection of thermal radiation

Thermal radiation is energy that is emitted by hot bodies. In most cases the chief constituent is infra-red radiation, but many hot objects obviously emit visible light and ultraviolet light. It can be shown that they also emit radio waves, although the amount of energy associated with radio waves is very small. All these forms of electromagnetic radiation (see the Unit *Vibrations and waves*) carry energy through space, and when they are absorbed by matter cause an increase in internal energy which usually results in a rise in temperature. This can cause a change in the physical properties of a material, which provides us with a means of detecting and measuring thermal radiation. One instrument used for this purpose is called a *bolometer*. It consists of a thin black strip of aluminium or semiconducting material. Radiation which is incident on the strip will cause its temperature to increase and the resulting change in electrical resistance can be measured. Another radiation detector is the *thermopile*, which consists of a number of thermocouples joined together in series.

Q 6.1 Study question
Make brief notes on the construction and principles of a thermopile. You should include details of the materials used, explain why one side is blackened, and describe the thermoelectric effect. ■

Q 6.2 Self-assessment question
Why does the exposed surface of a thermopile reach a steady temperature, despite the fact that it is continually receiving radiation? ■

6.2 Prévost's theory of exchanges

According to the ideas of Prévost, all bodies are not only continuously emitting thermal radiation but are also absorbing radiation from their surroundings. When a body is in thermal equilibrium with its surroundings (that is, they are at the same temperature), this energy exchange does not cease. The equilibrium is *dynamic*: the rate of emission of radiation to the surroundings is equal to the rate of absorption of radiation from the surroundings.

Note: In practice, even if the temperature is steady, the radiation emitted and the radiation absorbed by an object do not necessarily balance, because there may be a loss or gain of heat due to some other process (e.g. conduction or convection). For this reason, in theoretical considerations and in numerical problems, it is usual to consider an idealised system in which the body is supported by a non-conducting thread inside an evacuated space, in order to eliminate other forms of heat transfer.

Q 6.4 Study question
Describe how the experimental arrangement shown in figure 6.1 can be used to demonstrate Prévost's theory of exchanges. An object to act as a radiator (e.g. a blackened metal sphere) is placed at the focus of a concave mirror. A detector is placed at the focus of another concave mirror. Consider what happens when the metal sphere is warmed and when it is cooled. ■

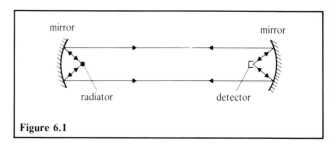

Figure 6.1

6.3 The ideal radiator

Uniform temperature enclosures

Thermal radiation is emitted (and absorbed) to a different extent by different kinds of surface.

Q 6.5 Self-assessment question
Which type of surface absorbs more radiation, a dull black surface or a polished white surface? ■

It follows from Prévost's theory of exchanges that good absorbers must also be good emitters.

Consider an enclosure whose walls are maintained at a constant temperature (figure 6.2). When a body at a different temperature is placed in the enclosure it will ultimately attain the temperature of the enclosure, irrespective of the nature of its surface or its original temperature.

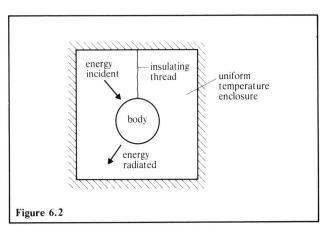

Figure 6.2

Q **6.6 Development question***
Suppose that three similar bodies (A, B and C) with different kinds of surface are placed in turn in the enclosure.
(a) A has a dull black surface. What can you say about most of the radiation that falls on it? Why does it follow from this that A will be a good emitter of radiation?
(b) B is highly polished. What can you say about most of the radiation that falls on it? Why does it follow from this that B must be a poor emitter of radiation?
(c) C absorbs radiation within a particular waveband (that is, it selectively absorbs a particular kind of radiation). What can you say about the way in which body C radiates to the surroundings?∎

This suggests that there is a connection between the way in which a body emits radiation and the way in which it absorbs radiation at a given temperature. This was first realised by the German physicist Kirchhoff. (We will discuss these ideas quantitatively in section 6.5.)

The concept of a black body
Since a good absorber is a good emitter, it follows that the best emitter will be the best absorber. What type of surface is the best absorber? Such a surface would be one that absorbs all the radiation (of all wavelengths) that falls on it. A body having such a surface is an ideal radiator and is called a *black body*. The radiation that it emits is called *black body radiation*.

This is an idealised concept (like the ideal gas of the kinetic theory), which can be nearly realised in practice. It is invaluable for the formulation of the laws of radiation and is a useful standard to which other bodies can be compared.

Black body radiation
No actual surface is ideally black, but a lampblack surface (which absorbs about 97% of the incident radiation) comes very close to the ideal. However, black body conditions can be realised by having a small opening in a constant temperature enclosure.

Q **6.7 Development question***
Suppose that a fourth body, D, is placed in the constant temperature enclosure (figure 6.2). D is a black body. Why does it follow that the radiation inside the enclosure must be black body radiation?∎

A uniform temperature enclosure is not affected by the nature of the bodies which are placed in it, nor by the nature of the walls of the enclosure. The radiation in it depends only on the temperature of the enclosure and is known as *temperature* or *full* radiation.

Q **6.8 Study question**
(a) Explain why an enclosure with a small cavity, such as that illustrated in figure 6.3, is an almost perfect black body.
(b) If the surface of the enclosure is maintained at a constant temperature, how can we describe the radiation which is emitted from the hole in the enclosure?
(c) How would you devise a black body to radiate at a temperature of 2000 K?∎

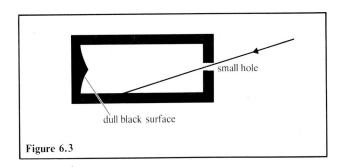

Figure 6.3

6.4 Stefan's law

The rate at which energy is being radiated from a body depends upon the *surface area* (the larger the area, the greater the power of the radiation emitted), the *nature of the surface* (a black surface is a better radiator than a white surface) and the *temperature*.

The way in which the rate of loss of energy (power radiated) from a black body depends upon the temperature was first formulated by Stefan in 1879. He suggested that it was proportional to the fourth power of the thermodynamic (absolute) temperature. He was led to this conclusion by consideration of the observations made by Tyndall, who found that the radiating powers of a heated platinum wire at 1200 °C and 525 °C were in the ratio of 11.7 to 1. Stefan suggested that the ratio

$$\left(\frac{1200 + 273}{525 + 273}\right)^4$$

was very nearly 11.7, and that the two radiating powers were thus proportional to the fourth power of the absolute temperature. Several years later Boltzmann, a pupil of Stefan's, showed that the relation could be deduced from theoretical considerations.

The fourth power law of radiation can be expressed as

→ $$M_B = \sigma T^4$$

where M_B is the power radiated over all wavelengths by a black body per unit surface area and T is the thermodynamic temperature. The constant of proportionality σ (pronounced sigma) is called the Stefan-Boltzmann constant.

Note: M is the total radiant exitance of the body; the subscript B refers to a black body. In some text books, the symbols E or P are used to denote this quantity.

The aim of this experiment is to investigate how heat is transferred by an electric lamp and to make an approximate verification of Stefan's fourth power law.

Q **6.9 Self-assessment question**
The radiant power Φ emitted by a filament is thought to be related to the temperature T of the filament by a law of the form $\Phi = AT^n$, where A and n are constants. A series of measurements of the electrical power input and the corresponding temperatures were taken to test this hypothesis.

Φ/W	0.25	1.39	3.91	10.20	21.00
T/K	400	600	800	1000	1200

(a) Draw a suitable graph to show whether the measurements confirm the hypothesis.
(b) Using your graph, find a value for n and estimate the probable error in your value.
(c) Find a value for A, giving the units in which it is measured.∎

Energy exchange between a body and its surroundings

Stefan's law applies to an isolated body. It would be more useful to have a formula which enables us to calculate the net exchange of radiation between a body and its surroundings. Consider a sphere P of surface area A at a temperature T enclosed by another sphere Q of surface area B at a temperature T_0 (figure 6.4). Suppose that both surfaces are perfect emitters and absorbers of radiation, that is, they are black bodies.

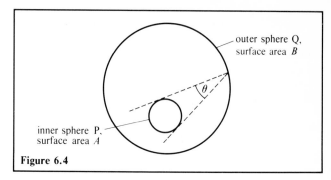

Figure 6.4

Q **6.10 Development question***
(a) Write down an expression for the total power Φ_A radiated by the inner sphere P.
(b) Write down an expression for the total power Φ_B radiated by the outer sphere Q.
(c) If T is greater than T_0, explain why the following statement is INCORRECT: 'The net power loss is given by $\Phi = \sigma(AT^4 - BT_0^4)$'.
(d) If the system was in thermal equilibrium, the inner sphere would be at the same temperature T_0 as its surroundings.
(i) Write down an expression for the total power radiated by the inner sphere.
(ii) What can you say about the power that the inner sphere absorbs from its surroundings?
(e) The power absorbed from the surroundings will be the same whether the system has reached thermal equilibrium or not, since it depends only on the temperature of the surroundings. If the temperature T of the inner sphere is higher than that of the surroundings, T_0, show that the net power loss is given by

$$\Phi_{net} = A\sigma T^4 - A\sigma T_0^4$$
$$= A\sigma(T^4 - T_0^4) \; ∎$$

The value of the Stefan-Boltzmann constant σ may be taken as 5.7×10^{-8} W m^{-2} K^{-4} in the following questions.

Q 6.11 Self-assessment question
A blackened sphere of radius 4.0 cm is inside a hollow evacuated enclosure, the walls of which are maintained at 300 K. Assuming that the sphere in the enclosure radiates like a black body, calculate the initial net power loss of the sphere when its temperature is 500 K. ∎

Notes: 1 If $T \gg T_0, \Phi_{net} \approx A\sigma T^4$.
2 If $(T - T_0)$ is small it can be shown that, for a black body, $\Phi_{net} \propto (T - T_0)$.

For small temperature differences, the rate of loss of heat by radiation is proportional to the excess temperature above the surroundings. This result is often assumed when making a cooling correction.

EXTENSION

Q 6.12 Study question
Show that, if $(T - T_0)$ is small,
$$\Phi = 4 A\sigma T_0^3 (T - T_0)$$
Hint: $(a^2 - b^2) = (a - b)(a + b)$, and $T \approx T_0$. ∎

To illustrate the use of Stefan's law, we will consider several practical applications, including radiation from a central heating 'radiator', and the energy absorbed by a solar heating panel.

Q 6.13 Self-assessment question
The surface area of a central heating radiator is 2.0 m^2, the water temperature is 47 °C and the temperature of the surroundings is 17 °C.
(a) Assuming that the surface of the radiator behaves like a black body and that the incoming radiation is black body radiation, calculate the net rate at which energy is being radiated to the surroundings.
(b) Describe briefly other ways in which heat is transferred to the surroundings. ∎

In practice, the surface of a central heating radiator is not a black body. This means that only a fraction of the black body radiation is emitted: the constant which determines this is called the *total emissivity*, ϵ, of the surface, and it has values between 0 and 1 (ϵ is defined in section 6.5). For a non-black body, the power radiated can be expressed as

→ $\quad \Phi = \epsilon A\sigma T^4$

Q 6.14 Self-assessment question
If the total emissivity of the surface of the radiator in question 6.13 is 0.6, calculate the net rate at which energy is being radiated to the surroundings, assuming that the temperature of the water is 67 °C. ∎

Q 6.15 Self-assessment question
Estimate the temperature of a 150 W tungsten filament lamp if the effective surface area of the filament is 50 mm^2 and the energy radiated is 0.4 of that from a corresponding black body. ∎

The following two questions are about the design of an electric lamp bulb. If a lamp is to operate at a certain temperature with a given p.d., how can we find the radius and the length of the filament?

Q 6.16 Self-assessment question
(a) Show that the power Φ radiated by the filament of the lamp is proportional to rlT^4, where r is the radius, l the length and T the temperature of the filament.
(b) For a given value of p.d., show that the rate at which electrical energy is transformed into internal energy is proportional to r^2/l.
(c) When conditions are steady, the rate at which energy is being transformed in the filament is equal to the rate at which energy is being radiated. Show how the temperature is related to the radius and length of the filament. ∎

Q 6.17 Self-assessment question
Suppose you wish to design a 60 W 12 V car headlamp bulb to operate at a temperature of 3000 K. What radius and length must the tungsten filament have?
(Resistivity of tungsten at 3000 K = $7.0 \times 10^{-7} \Omega$ m.) ∎

Solar energy

Increasing concern for the preservation of our environment and the fact that the world's resources of fossil fuels are very limited, has given renewed impetus to the development of ways of utilising the sun's energy. The power received from the sun by the earth per unit area of surface placed normally to the radiation, when absorption losses in the earth's atmosphere have been corrected for, is known as the *solar constant, S*. Its value is found by experiment to be 1.35×10^3 W m^{-2}.

Q **6.18 Study question***
Estimate the rate at which energy is absorbed per unit area by a black body on the earth's surface, such as a solar heating panel placed so that the sun's rays fall normally on it. Neglect the effect of the earth's atmosphere.

Black body temperature of sun, $T = 6000$ K,
radius of sun, $r = 7.0 \times 10^8$ m,
mean distance from earth to sun, $R = 1.5 \times 10^{11}$ m,
Stefan-Boltzman constant, $\sigma = 5.7 \times 10^{-8}$ W m^{-2} K^{-4}. ∎

Q **6.19 Self-assessment question**
A solar heating panel covers an area of 20 m² and the efficiency of the system is 60%. Assuming that on a clear day 600 W m^{-2} of solar energy are received, calculate the time required to increase the temperature of 5 m³ of water from 0 °C to 60 °C.
(The density of water $= 10^3$ kg m^{-3}, the specific heat capacity of water $= 4.2 \times 10^3$ J kg^{-1} K^{-1}.) ∎

Even allowing for the fact that some of the sun's radiation is reflected by the atmosphere and some is absorbed, there is still available approximately 0.75 kW m^{-2} at the earth's surface. However, our present technology cannot provide us with *economic* methods of direct conversion of solar radiation into usable energy (i.e. electrical energy). It is still cheaper to burn coal or even oil, because of the high cost of constructing a solar power station. Many schemes are, however, being used; the use of parabolic reflectors to concentrate the sun's rays to produce a solar furnace, solar cells to produce electricity and the use of solar panels to provide domestic heating (figure 6.5).

Figure 6.5

EXTENSION

Q **6.20 Study question**
Imagine that you have recently joined a research team that is investigating the practical applications of solar energy. Prepare a report on the use of solar energy for domestic heating. ∎

6.5 Distribution of energy with wavelength

The way in which the energy radiated from a black body varies with wavelength and the temperature of the body was first investigated by Lummer and Pringsheim in 1893. The analysis of their results which follows is important, because new ideas about the emission of radiation were introduced in order to explain the observations.

Figure 6.6 shows diagrammatically the arrangement of their apparatus. The radiation from a black body, at a certain temperature, was spread out by means of the prism to form a spectrum. When the thermopile was moved along the spectrum, it showed a maximum reading at a particular part of the spectrum. When the temperature of the source was increased, the maximum reading was found to be at a different part of the spectrum.

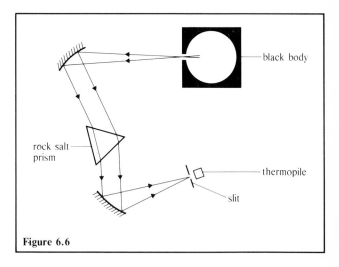

Figure 6.6

When the detector is at a particular place in the spectrum, it receives energy from a narrow waveband. It does not receive the energy at just a single wavelength. Figure 6.7 is a graph which shows how the energy within a discrete waveband varies with wavelength, for a particular temperature of the black body. It is known as a distribution curve (see Appendix 2).

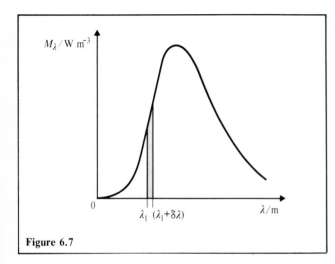

Figure 6.7

To describe how the energy is distributed we must define the quantity M_λ which is plotted on the y-axis. It is called the *spectral radiant exitance*.

$M_\lambda \, \delta\lambda$ is the power radiated (or the energy radiated per second) per unit area of surface in the waveband λ to $\lambda + \delta\lambda$, so

$$M_\lambda \, \delta\lambda = \Phi/A$$

The units of M_λ are W m^{-2} m^{-1} = W m^{-3}. When considering a black body we will use the symbol $M_{\lambda, B}$.

Q 6.21 Development question*
(a) What does the curve show about the way in which the power radiated by a black body varies with wavelength?
(b) (i) What does the area of the shaded strip represent?
(ii) What are the units of this quantity?

(c) What does the total area underneath the graph represent?
(d) How must this area depend on the thermodynamic (absolute) temperature?
(e) In an experiment to measure the energy distribution, what determines the size of the waveband?■

SYLLABUS EXTENSION

Q 6.22 Study question
Describe briefly how the distribution of energy in the spectrum of a black body has been investigated experimentally. You should include details of the source, an explanation of why it is a reasonable black body, comments on the dispersing system and on methods of detection.■

Wien's displacement law

Q 6.23 Development question
Figure 6.8 shows the energy distribution for three different black body temperatures. What happens to the wavelength λ_{max}, for which the energy radiated is a maximum, as the temperature is increased?■

Note: You are required to be able to sketch curves which show how the energy radiated from a black body varies with wavelength and explain the features of these curves.

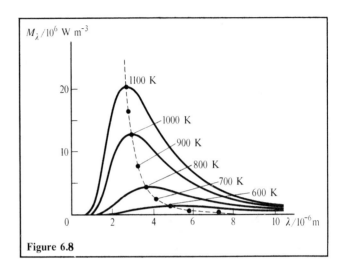

Figure 6.8

Prior to the work of Lummer and Pringsheim, Wien had shown theoretically that for black body radiation the wavelength λ_{max} for a given value of absolute temperature was given by

$$\lambda_{max} \, T = \text{constant}$$

This is known as Wien's displacement law and the value of the constant (which is determined by experiment) is 2.9×10^{-3} m K.

Q 6.24 Self-assessment question
How does the colour of the visible light radiated by a very hot body change as the temperature of the body increases?■

Q 6.25 Self-assessment question
Estimate the black body temperature of the sun, given that the wavelength at which the energy in the solar spectrum is a maximum is 4.9×10^{-7} m.■

Note: The sun's temperature can also be estimated by applying Stefan's law to the total radiation emitted. This involves an experimental determination of the solar constant. (In question 6.18 we assumed a value for the temperature of the sun and made an estimate of the solar constant.)

EXTENSION

Pyrometers

High temperatures (for example, greater than 1000 °C) are usually measured by observing the radiation from the hot body (figure 6.9). The name pyrometry is given to this type of measurement.

Q 6.26 Study question
Make notes on the construction and principle of the disappearing filament optical pyrometer and explain how it is calibrated.■

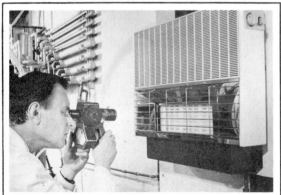

Figure 6.9

Emission and absorption of radiation

So far we have been mainly concerned with the power radiated by a black body. However, in practice, sources which have the same surface area and the same temperature may radiate or absorb heat at different rates. (A dull black surface will radiate more heat, and absorb more heat, than a white polished surface.) For this reason it is valuable to compare the way in which a non-black body radiates with the behaviour of a black body at the same temperature.

Q 6.27 Development question*
The graphs in figure 6.10 show the results of an experiment to compare the energy distribution with wavelength of a non-black body with that of a black body at the same temperature T.
(a) Comment on the features of the curves.
(b) How would you obtain (i) the total power radiated per unit area by the non-black body, (ii) the ratio of M, the total power radiated per unit area by the non-black body, to M_B, the total power radiated per unit area by a black body at the same temperature?
(c) The ratio that you have indicated is called the total emissivity ϵ of the body. Write down an equation which defines ϵ.
(d) Suppose that the non-black body was in a uniform temperature enclosure at a temperature T. Why is the area underneath the non-black body curve equal to the total power absorbed per unit area by the non-black body?
(e) We define the total absorptance α as the ratio of the total power absorbed by the surface to the total power incident on the surface. Derive a relationship between the total emissivity and the total absorptance.■

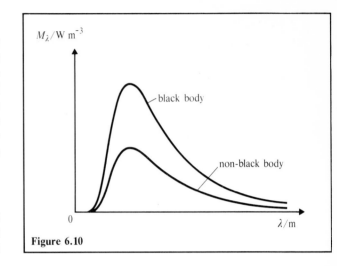

Figure 6.10

Q 6.28 Self-assessment question
(a) What is the total emissivity of (i) a perfect reflector, and (ii) a black body?
(b) What is the total absorptance of (i) a perfect reflector, and (ii) a black body?■

Spectral emissivity

Many surfaces and bodies are coloured. This means that they reflect or transmit some wavelengths better than others. A material such as glass will transmit infra-red radiation of short wavelength but absorbs infra-red radiation of longer wavelength.

Q 6.29 Development question*

Figure 6.11 shows how the energy distribution of another non-black body varies with wavelength, compared to that of a black body at the same temperature T.

(a) Comment on the features of these curves?
(b) What does the area ABDC represent?
(c) What does the area ABFE represent? ■

The ratio of the areas ABDC and ABFE is called the *spectral emissivity* ϵ_λ of the surface. This is defined as the ratio of the power radiated by a body per unit area in the waveband λ to $\lambda + \delta\lambda$ to the power radiated by a black body per unit area in the same waveband at the same temperature, or

$$\epsilon_\lambda = M_\lambda / M_{\lambda,B}$$

The *spectral absorptance* α_λ of a surface is defined as the ratio of the power absorbed in the waveband λ to $\lambda + \delta\lambda$ to the power incident on the surface in the same waveband.

Q 6.30 Self-assessment question

Assuming that the non-black body is in a uniform temperature enclosure at a temperature T and receives radiation in the waveband λ to $\lambda + \delta\lambda$, derive a relationship between ϵ_λ and α_λ. ■

Q 6.31 Study question

Figure 6.12 shows the relative intensity of the emission spectrum of a material. When white light passes through the vapour of this material, there is a dark line in the continuous spectrum. Explain. ■

Q 6.32 Study question

Explain why glass is suitable for the construction of a greenhouse. ■

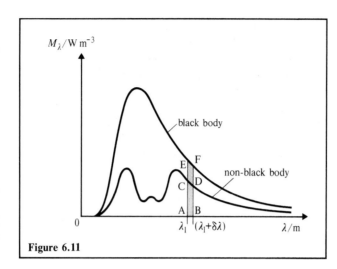

Figure 6.11

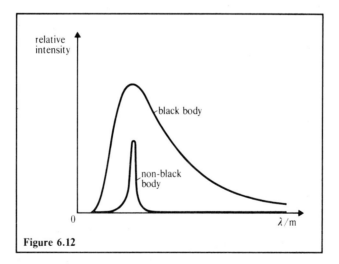

Figure 6.12

Birth of the quantum theory

At the end of the nineteenth century, several attempts were made to explain and derive formulae to describe how the energy radiated by a black body depends upon wavelength and temperature.

The problem was that theories put forward to explain the energy distribution in the radiation from a black body could not explain why the curves shown in figure 6.8 had a maximum value which was determined by the absolute temperature of the body.

It was solved by a German physicist, Max Planck, who published a paper in 1900 which described an equation which fitted the experimental results. In order to do this, he had to introduce new ideas about the nature of radiation. (In fact, most scientists of his day treated his ideas as a joke!) He assumed, with no obvious justification, that energy is emitted and absorbed in discrete packets or quanta and that the energy E of each packet or quantum was given by the relationship

$$E = h\nu$$

where h is a constant called the Planck constant and ν is the frequency of the radiation.

Four years later Einstein published a paper which showed how this same assumption could be used to explain the photoelectric effect, that is, the emission of electrons from metals by light. (This is discussed in the Unit *Electrons and the nucleus*.) These two papers marked the beginnings of *quantum theory*, a way of thinking which has become crucial in many branches of advanced physics, replacing the classical mechanics.

Comprehension exercise

MEDICAL THERMOGRAPHY
(Freely adapted from 'Medical Thermography' *Scientific American,* February 1967.)

The idea of taking a sick person's temperature in order to gain information about his condition is well known, though the accurate measurement of body temperatures is in fact less than a hundred years old. More recently the concept has been given a new dimension through a technique known as thermography which relies on the fact that the temperature of the skin can vary from place to place and in consequence the heat radiated from different parts varies both in quality and quantity.

To appreciate the process one needs to realise that infrared radiation emitted by the skin obeys the same laws as other electromagnetic waves. Thus every body at a temperature higher than absolute zero emits radiant energy from its surface. The wavelength and intensity depend on the absolute temperature of the object and the total emissivity of its surface. The total emissivity is the name given to that property of a surface which determines the rate at which it loses heat by radiation. The law of Physics which describes quantitatively the rate of loss of heat from a body by radiation states that the power radiated Φ (or the energy radiated per second) is given by the expression $\Phi = \epsilon \sigma A T^4$, where ϵ is the total emissivity, A is the area of the surface, T is the absolute temperature of the surface and σ is the Stefan-Boltzmann constant. Thus if the total emissivity is constant the energy received per second by a suitably placed detector will be proportional to the fourth power of the absolute temperature of the surface from which the radiation is emitted.

The object of thermography is to convert measurements of this radiated energy from different places into values of temperature. With sensitive apparatus the differences in the infrared radiation can be registered on thermograms as a series of dots that are black, some shade of gray or white according as the temperature of the corresponding point on the object is low, moderate or high.

In one type of apparatus the radiation from the body falls first on a front silvered plane mirror and is then focused by means of a system of curved mirrors onto a thermistor carrying an electric current. The thermistor is made of a substance whose electrical resistance decreases with rise in temperature in such a way that if the temperature rises by 1 K the resistance decreases by 4% of its value at the lower temperature. The flow of this radiation onto the thermistor is interrupted by a chopper so that the thermistor receives, in turn, radiation from the mirrors and radiation from parts of the chopper itself which has a special black surface. The chopper can consist of a rotating disc with alternate sectors cut away. This arrangement means that the potential difference across the thermistor fluctuates and these fluctuations, after considerable amplification, can be made to light a gas discharge tube which then glows with an intensity related to the radiant energy falling on the thermistor from the skin.

It remains to be explained how the body area to be investigated is scanned. This is done by rocking the plane mirror on which the radiation first falls in such a way that the object is first swept horizontally and the mirror then returns to very nearly its starting point during which time the discharge tube is dark. During this time also the mirror is tipped slightly so that the next horizontal traverse is just below the first. A complete scan covers about 20° in the horizontal direction and 10° in the vertical and takes about 4 minutes.

The light from the discharge tube falls on the back of the original plane mirror which is also silvered and is reflected from there into a suitable camera.

Alongside the patient are one or more heat radiators maintained at standard temperatures and images of these appear alongside images of the patient on the thermogram. They enable temperatures of parts of the body to be determined to within 0.5 K.

Questions

1 Explain with reference to the properties of waves, what is meant by the statement that radiation from different parts of the body may differ 'in quality and quantity'.

2 Sketch a graph to show how the total energy radiated per second by a body varies with its absolute temperature.

3 (a) Draw a diagram in which, apart from the plane mirror, each portion of the apparatus is represented by a labelled box, the boxes being linked to indicate the sequence of events whereby the apparatus converts radiation from the human body into a photographic image.
(b) What advantages are gained by using both sides of the plane mirror?

4 Indicate by means of a ray diagram how the radiation diverging from the plane mirror could be focused onto the thermistor by a suitably designed arrangement of a concave and a convex mirror. Why is this arrangement of mirrors likely to be preferable to a convex lens which at first sight would appear to be simpler?

5 (a) If the total emissivity of human skin is assumed to be 0.97, calculate the total energy radiated in one minute by an area of 0.01 m² at a temperature of 310 K. The Stefan-Boltzmann constant is 5.7×10^{-8} W m^{-2} K^{-4}.

(b) It is sometimes assumed that a human being in a room is equivalent to a heater of about 1 kW in the room. Use the data given and/or your answer to part (a) of this question to determine whether or not this assumption is reasonable.

6 Use the information in the first half of paragraph 4 to sketch a graph showing how the resistance of a thermistor varies over a range of temperature of about 50 K. Explain how the shape of your graph follows from the information in the text.

(b) Discuss **two** reasons why you would expect the thermistor to be small.

7 Why is a discharge tube used in preference to a filament lamp?

8 Why are the standard radiators mentioned in the last paragraph important?

Questions on objectives

1 Give a short account of Prévost's theory of exchanges. Show, by considering surfaces in a uniform temperature enclosure, how it leads to the conclusion that a dull black surface which is a good absorber of radiation is also a good emitter of radiation.

(objectives 4 and 9)

2 Explain what is meant by a perfectly black body. Why does a small hole in a uniform temperature enclosure approximate to a perfect radiator?

(objective 5)

3 (a) State Stefan's law.

(b) A perfectly black body at a high temperature is in surroundings at a lower temperature. Give an equation for its net power loss. Define the symbols in your equation and state a consistent set of units for them.

(objectives 2, 4 and 6)

4 Draw curves to show how the energy radiated by a black body varies with wavelength for two different temperatures. Indicate which is the higher temperature. Explain what quantity is plotted against wavelength.

(objective 7)

5 The surface area of the radiator bar of a 1.0 kW electric fire is 0.027 m². If the temperature of the surroundings is 290 K, estimate the working temperature of the radiating bar. Give two reasons why the actual temperature is likely to differ from your estimate.

(objectives 9 and 10)

6 The total surface area of a series of solar panels is 10^3 m². Calculate the quantity I of solar energy which falls on the panels per minute, assuming that half is absorbed or reflected by the earth's atmosphere and that the panels are normal to the sun's rays.

Temperature of sun's surface, $T = 6000$ K,
radius of sun, $r = 7.5 \times 10^8$ m,
mean distance of sun from earth, $R = 1.5 \times 10^{11}$ m,
Stefan-Boltzmann constant, $\sigma = 5.7 \times 10^{-8}$ W m^{-2} K^{-4},
total emissivity of panels, $\epsilon = 0.95$

(objective 10)

Appendixes

Appendix 1: Distribution curves

Figure A1 is a typical graph of the relationship between two continuously varying quantities, in this case, pressure and volume of a gas at a fixed temperature. It enables us to know the value of the pressure for *any* value of volume over the range of the graph.

Figure A2 is a different kind of graph, called a histogram. It tells us about the speed of vehicles passing a recording point on a motor-way. Suppose we count the number of cars passing in a fixed interval. The histogram records the number of cars passing during this interval in a particular speed range (e.g. 50–60 m s^{-1}). Each rectangle indicates by its height or area the number of vehicles in a particular speed range. Although the horizontal axis marks speed it cannot be read like an ordinary graph. The speed axis does not change continuously, but in steps from one speed range to the next. The graph cannot tell us whether any cars had a speed of 68.5 m s^{-1} past the recording point – only the number of cars in different groups. To obtain more detailed information we would need to divide the speed into smaller and smaller ranges and take readings for thousands of vehicles. Then we might get a graph like figure A3. In this graph the vertical axis is changed, so that now the *area* of each strip can be made to represent the number of cars passing in the given time in a very narrow speed range. The area of the shaded strip records that 14 cars passed with speeds between 62 and 64 m s^{-1} (7 cars s m^{-1} × 2 m s^{-1} = 14 cars).

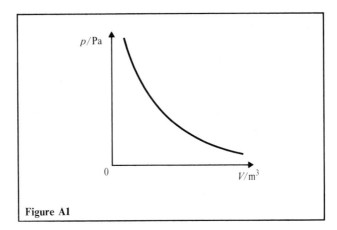

Figure A1

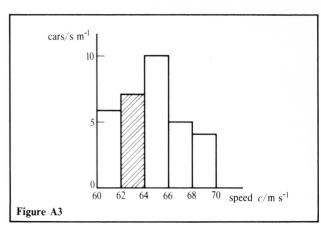

Figure A3

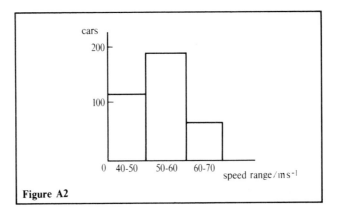

Figure A2

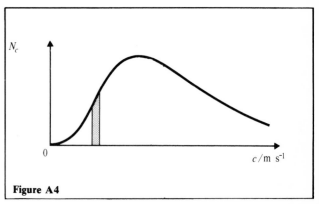

Figure A4

Q A1 What would the total area of all the strips in figure A3 represent? Use figure A3 to estimate this quantity and say whether figure A2 might be recording the same data in the 60–70 m.p.h. range.■

In studying gases we are dealing with so many molecules that their speeds can be represented by a smooth distribution curve, and the area of any strip under the curve represents the number of molecules in that speed range (figure A4). Consider what the vertical axis represents in figure A4. It is labelled N_c.

Since the number of molecules in a given speed range is represented by the area of a strip, we can write

$$\text{number of molecules with speeds between } c \text{ and } c + \delta c = N_c \, \delta c$$

Q A2 The speed range δc will have units m s^{-1}. What is the unit of N_c? What does the shaded area in figure A4 represent? What are the units of this area?■

Distribution curves of energy radiated in different wavelength ranges will be discussed in this and other APPIL Units, and the same rules apply in interpreting the graphs. A distribution curve can be obtained experimentally by measuring the value of the variable in a discrete range. For example, the energy passing through a slit will indicate the energy in a discrete wavelength range and a series of values throughout the spectrum will provide information to construct a distribution curve.

Appendix 2:
The mole

When comparing the behaviour of different substances, it is very helpful to be able to consider a quantity of matter which always contains the same number of entities (particles or specified groups of particles), whatever the substance. The mole is such a quantity.

The mole is defined as the amount of a substance which contains as many particles (atoms, molecules or ions) as there are carbon atoms in 0.012 kg of carbon 12.

This number of particles is known as the Avogadro constant N_A and its value is $6.022 \times 10^{23} \text{ mol}^{-1}$. The molar mass of helium, that is, the mass of 6.02×10^{23} particles (atoms), is $4 \times 10^{-3} \text{ kg mol}^{-1}$. The molar mass of molecular oxygen (the mass of 6.02×10^{23} molecules or 12.04×10^{23} atoms) is $32 \times 10^{-3} \text{ kg mol}^{-1}$. In general, if M_r is the relative molecular mass, then a mole of these molecules has a mass of $M_r \times 10^{-3} \text{ kg}$.

Experimental evidence and the kinetic theory of gases are both in agreement with Avogadro's law. A mole of any ideal gas will exert the same pressure if the volumes and temperatures are equal. It is found that one mole of an ideal gas will occupy 22.4 litres (0.0224 m³) at standard temperature (273.15 K) and standard pressure (1.013×10^5 Pa).

Q A3 What value of the molar gas constant R is predicted by the results stated in the last sentence? What is the unit of R?■

Q A4 What is the volume occupied by $2.2 \times 10^{-3} \text{ kg}$ of CO_2 at s.t.p. if the relative atomic masses of carbon and oxygen are 12 and 16 respectively?■

Experiment TP1   Specific heat capacity - electrical method

Aim

In this experiment you will determine the specific heat capacity of a liquid and estimate the errors involved in the measurement.

Apparatus

- calorimeter, lagging and bung
- thermometer, 0–50 °C in 0.2 °C
- stirrer
- liquid (e.g. paraffin oil or glycerine)
- l.t. variable power supply
- heating coil
- ammeter, 0–10 A
- voltmeter, 0–15 V
- variable resistor, 0–15 Ω
- chemical balance

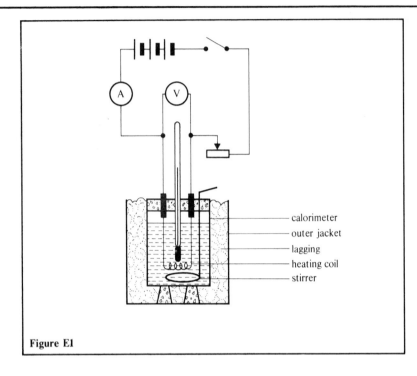

calorimeter
outer jacket
lagging
heating coil
stirrer

Figure E1

1   Weigh a dry calorimeter and stirrer and record its mass m_c.

2   Pour in liquid so that there is enough to cover the elemen re-weigh and record the new mass ($m_c + m$), where m is the mass of th liquid.

3   Set up the apparatus as shown in figure E1.

4   Switch on the current and adjust the variable resistor so that th current is about 2 A. Switch off. Stir the liquid and wait until th temperature of the liquid is equal to room temperature.

5   Read the temperature of the liquid θ_1 and then switch on th current and start a stop-watch simultaneously. Record the current I *Note*: While the liquid heats up you should stir it regularly and keep th ammeter reading constant by means of the variable resistor.

6   Record the temperature θ and the p.d. V every half minute.

7   After the temperature has risen about 10 °C, switch off th current and record the time t but continue recording the temperatu every half minute for a further time t.

8   Plot a graph of temperature (y-axis) against time (x-axis).

9   From the graph find
(a) the maximum temperature θ_2 reached by the liquid,
(b) the time t_1, which may not be exactly equal to t, to reach th temperature,
(c) the fall in temperature θ_c occurring in a time $t_1/2$. θ_c is the cooli correction to be added to θ_2.

10   Calculate a value for the specific heat capacity of the liqui (Specific heat capacity of copper is 3.9×10^2 J kg^{-1} K^{-1}.)

11   Explain briefly why a cooling correction is necessary in this expe iment.

12   Estimate the percentage error in your value of the specific he capacity of the liquid.

Experiment TP2   Specific heat capacity - continuous flow method

Aim
In this experiment you will determine the specific heat capacity of water by a continuous flow method.

Apparatus
constant flow apparatus
constant head tank
2 thermometers, 0–50 °C in 0.2 °C
stop-watch
ammeter, 0–10 A
voltmeter, 0–15 V
variable resistor, 0–15 Ω
l.t. variable power supply
chemical balance

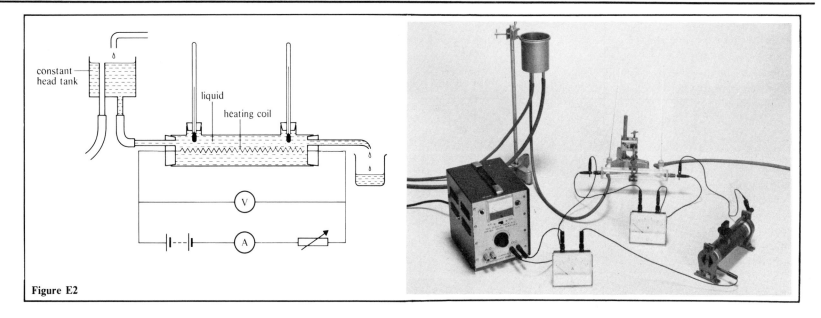

Figure E2

1   Set up the apparatus as shown in figure E2.

2   Adjust the rate of flow of water and/or the potential difference across the heating coil until you get about a 5 °C difference in the steady temperature readings of the thermometers.
Why do the thermometers reach a steady reading?

3   Allow the water to flow for some time (to enable the steady conditions to become established) and collect the water in a weighed beaker for about 2 minutes.

4   Record, under steady conditions, the following quantities: potential difference V_1, current I_1, temperature of water entering θ_1, temperature of water leaving θ_2, mass of water collected m_1, time for collection of water t.

5   Now repeat steps 2 and 3, using a different flow rate and adjusting the potential difference so that the thermometers give the *same steady readings* as before (this is quite tricky to achieve). Collect the water flowing for the same time t.

6   Record the new values of the potential difference V_2, current I_2, and the mass of water collected m_2. Then, if Q is the energy loss to the surroundings in time t, and c is the specific heat capacity of the water,

$$I_1 V_1 t = m_1 c (\theta_2 - \theta_1) + Q$$
$$\text{and } I_2 V_2 t = m_2 c (\theta_2 - \theta_1) + Q$$

Eliminate Q from these two equations and calculate a value for c.

7   Discuss the errors that still exist in this experiment and suggest any ways in which these could be reduced.

Aim

The aim of this experiment is to determine a value for the specific latent heat of vaporisation of water by a continuous flow method.

Apparatus

- vacuum flask
- heating coil
- delivery tube
- Liebig condenser
- chemical balance
- conical flask
- ammeter, 0–5 A
- voltmeter, 0–30 V
- stop-clock or watch
- beaker
- l.t. variable power supply
- variable resistor, 0–15 Ω

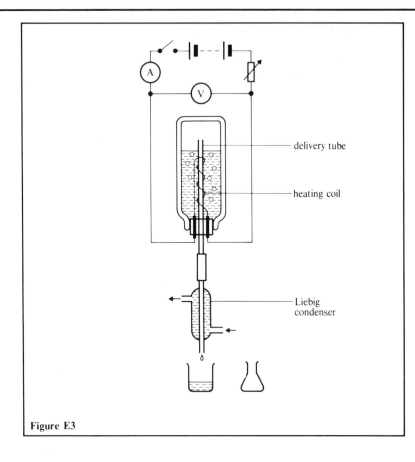

delivery tube

heating coil

Liebig condenser

Figure E3

1   Fill the vacuum flask with hot water so that the heating coil will be well covered when the flask is inverted.

2   Arrange the apparatus as shown in figure E3.

3   Switch on the current and, by means of the variable resistor, adjust the current to about 2.5 A (this value will depend upon your heating coil).

4   Allow the water to boil for several minutes. When the condensed steam is passing steadily into the beaker, replace it by the weighed conical flask and start the stop-watch. Keep the current constant and record the p.d. across the heating coil at regular intervals. When a reasonable quantity of condensed steam has been collected, remove the flask and stop the stop-watch. Replace the beaker under the delivery tube and re-weigh the flask to determine the mass of steam that has condensed.

5   Adjust the variable resistor so that the current is about three quarters of its previous value and repeat step 4, collecting the condensed steam for the same time.

6   From your results calculate a value for the specific latent heat of vaporisation of water.

7   How accurately can you measure the current, p.d., mass of liquid and temperature?

8   Why can you assume that l is the same in the two experiments?

9   What are the advantages of this method compared to one in which steam is allowed to condense in water contained in a calorimeter (method of mixtures)?

Experiment TP4 Effect of pressure on the volume of a gas at constant temperature

Aim

In this experiment you will measure the changes in the volume of air enclosed in a gas syringe when the pressure acting on the gas is changed.

Apparatus

large gas syringe (100 ml glass type)
weights, 0–4 kg in ½ kg steps
thin rubber tube with screw clip, or syringe cap
retort stands and clamps
pulley and string
vacuum grease, or vacuum pump oil and vaseline

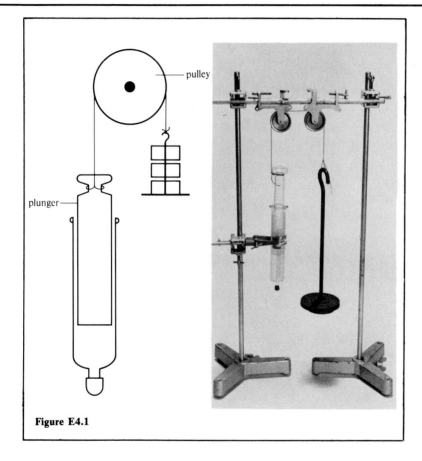

Figure E4.1

Note: Read through the whole experiment before beginning your observations, and draw up a table for recording your results in the form shown

Load m/kg	Force F/N acting on the gas	Excess pressure p/Pa	Volume of gas V/cm^3			V^{-1}/ cm$^-$
			loading	unloading	average volume	
1	2	3	4	5	6	7

1   Grease the sides of the gas syringe plunger with vacuum grease or a mixture of vacuum pump oil and vaseline so that the plunger moves smoothly without sticking. Clamp the syringe firmly and vertically. Move the plunger until the syringe contains 50 cm^3 of air, then seal the outlet tube. Is the gas in the syringe at atmospheric pressure? Explain your answer.

2   Attach a string to the plunger as shown in figure E4.1, pass it over a well-lubricated pulley and attach a load to the string. Make sure that the string from the plunger is vertical and that the load is freely suspended. Observe the volume of gas in the syringe for about 30 s after adding a load of 1 kg and record the volume when it has become constant (column 4). Record the load (column 1).

3   Record the volume of the enclosed gas as further 1 kg masses are added to the load, up to 4 kg (columns 1 and 4).

4   Record the volume of the gas as the kilogram masses are removed (column 5). Why is it a good idea to make two sets of readings for volume (columns 4 and 5)?

Continued overleaf

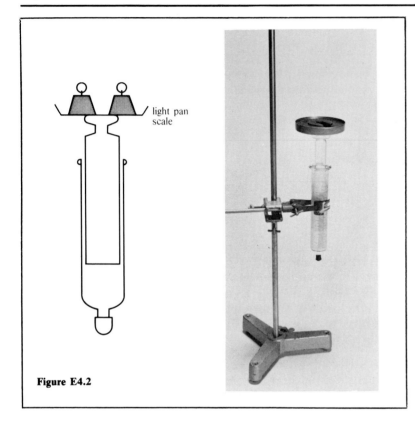

light pan
scale

Figure E4.2

5   Now use plasticine to attach a light scale pan to the plunger (figure E4.2) in order to load the gas so that it is compressed. Again record the volume as the mass on the scale pan is increased to 4 kg and then decreased.

6   Calculate the force F acting on the gas due to each load, and record it as *negative* when the piston is being pulled up and *positive* when the gas is being compressed (column 2).

7   Is the mass of the plasticine, scale pan, or plunger significant in calculating force F? Give reasons for your decision and correct the value of F if these factors are important.

8   Calculate and record the cross-sectional area A of the syringe by measuring the separation of the graduations.

9   Calculate the excess pressure p acting on the gas due to the load and record these values in the table (column 3).

10   Plot a graph of excess pressure (y-axis) against 1/volume (x-axis) for both positive and negative values of excess pressure. Choose the scales so that the $1/V$ axis starts at zero and the negative excess pressure axis extends to 10^5 Pa.

11   If the air in the syringe obeys Boyle's law, since
total gas pressure = atmospheric pressure (P) + excess pressure (p)
then $(P + p)\,V$ = constant.

What sort of a graph would you expect if you plotted excess pressure against $1/V$? What should the intercept on the pressure axis be?

12   Does your graph suggest that the air in the syringe obeys Boyle's law? What value do you obtain for the atmospheric pressure from your graph?

13   The air enclosed in the syringe has been used as a barometer to measure atmospheric pressure. Could the gas syringe be used as a thermometer? Say briefly how.

Experiment TP5 Measurement of temperature by a gas thermometer

Aim

A simple constant volume gas thermometer is calibrated at the ice and steam points and then used to measure the temperature of the room and of a solution of brine.

Apparatus

- glass bulb connected to mercury manometer and metre scale (pressure law apparatus or gas thermometer)
- large glass beaker
- tripod, gauze, bunsen burner
- ice
- common salt

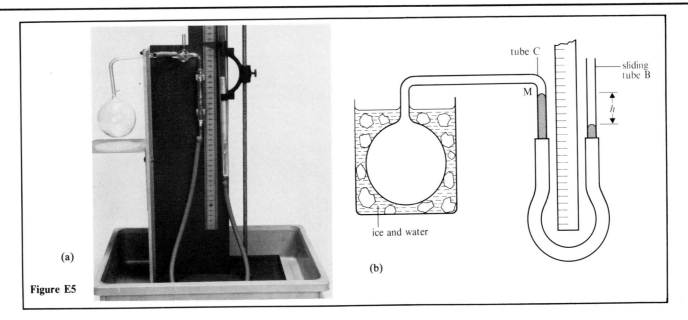

(a)

(b)

Figure E5

1   With the bulb at room temperature (figure E5a) adjust the position of sliding tube B (figure E5b) so that the mercury level in tube C is at the fixed mark M. Record the scale reading for the fixed mark M and the level of the mercury in tube B.

2   Lower the sliding tube B so that the mercury falls a long way below mark M. Place the bulb A in the beaker so that it is completely surrounded by the ice and water mixture. Wait for the temperature of the bulb to become constant. How will you know when this has been achieved? Adjust B until the mercury level in C is again at the fixed mark M. Note the reading of the level of mercury in tube B.

3   Now heat the beaker and its contents until the water boils steadily. Record the reading of the level of mercury in tube B, after adjusting the level in C to mark M.

4   Add 20 g of salt to the water in the beaker and record the reading of the level of mercury in tube B after the liquid in the beaker has been boiling steadily for a few minutes. The readings can be repeated after adding more salt.

5   Calculate the excess height h of mercury in the open tube B at the different temperatures.
Note: When the level of the mercury in tube B is below M the excess height is negative.

6   Draw a calibration graph of excess height against temperature by marking in the values of h at the ice and steam points. Use this graph to measure the room temperature and the boiling point of the brine.

Experiment TP6 Variation of s.v.p. of water with temperature

Aim

The boiling point of water will be measured at different pressures and the results used to plot a graph of s.v.p. against temperature.

Apparatus

- Bourdon gauge
- rubber pressure tubing
- round-bottomed flask, 250 cm³
- thermometer, −10 to 110 °C
- T-piece
- bung with 2 holes (for thermometer and T-piece)
- Hoffman clip
- bunsen burner
- tripod
- gauze
- pieces of broken pot
- retort stand and clamp

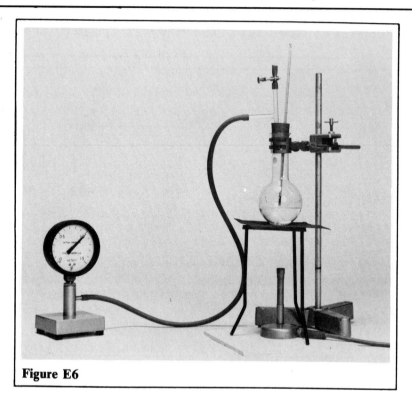

Figure E6

1 The flask, supported by a retort stand and clamp, contains a little water and some pieces of broken pot. The thermometer should just touch the water surface. The gauge is joined to the T-piece by a short length of pressure tubing (figure E6).

2 Boil the water for several minutes with the clip *open* to drive out as much air as possible. Remove the flame and, when boiling stops, *immediately* close the clip tightly.

3 Remove the tripod and warm the flask *gently* with a *small* flame until the water just boils. Record the temperature and pressure at which this happens.
Note: Tap the gauge before reading.

4 Repeat this sequence at lower temperatures and pressures by allowing the flask to cook for a longer period before warming it again. A series of readings of boiling point and pressure should be tabulated.
Note: Boil the water as briefly as possible to reduce condensation inside the gauge.

5 Plot a graph of the s.v.p. of water against temperature.

6 In calibrating a thermometer at the steam point, an error of 4 mm was involved in the measurement of pressure by a mercury barometer (4 mmHg pressure is approximately equal to 600 Pa). Use your graph to estimate the error introduced in the calibration of the thermometer at the 100 °C mark.

Experiment TP7 Heat loss of a filament lamp

Aim

The aim of this experiment is to investigate how heat is lost by a filament lamp and make an approximate verification of Stefan's fourth power law.

Apparatus

- tungsten filament lamp, 36 W 12 V
- ammeter, 0–10 A
- voltmeter, 0–15 V
- variable resistor, 0–15 Ω
- calorimeter
- leads
- switch

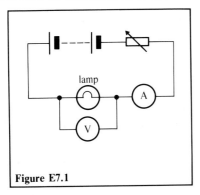

Figure E7.1

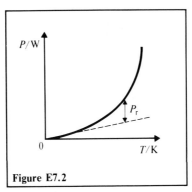

Figure E7.2

1 Set up the circuit as shown in figure E7.1. Support the lamp in a calorimeter which contains cold water. Ensure that it is completely immersed.

2 Switch on the current and obtain a series of readings for the current I and the potential difference V. Make sure that a steady state has been reached each time before taking the readings.

Note: Begin with very small currents and continue to the largest current for which the lamp is designed. (You could go beyond this, but only at the risk of 'blowing' the lamp.)

3 Calculate the power that is required to keep the filament at a particular temperature and the corresponding resistance of the filament. Calculate the temperature θ of the filament using the relationship

$$R_\theta = R_0 (1 + \alpha\theta)$$

where R_θ is the resistance at a temperature θ, and R_0 is the resistance at 0 °C (and may be assumed to be equal to the resistance of the filament for very small currents). α is the temperature coefficient of resistance

of tungsten and may be taken as 5.2×10^{-3} K^{-1}.

4 Plot a graph of the power P (y-axis) against the corresponding (absolute) temperature T (x-axis).

5 The electric power supplied is equal to the heat lost per second. This heat loss is in two parts; a loss by conduction through the gas surrounding the filament and a loss by radiation. Figure E7.2 shows the form of the graph that you may have obtained. In the straight part of the graph the heat loss is mainly due to conduction, whereas in the curved part the heat loss is due to radiation.

Note: You may find that the heat loss due to conduction is very small.

The electrical power supplied at any temperature of the filament is equal to the sum of the losses by conduction and by radiation:

$$P = k_1 (T - T_0) + k_2 (T^n - T_0^n)$$

where k_1 and k_2 are constants, T and T_0 the temperatures of the filament and surrounding water respectively, and the exponent n is the unknown to be found from the experiment.

The heat loss by radiation can be found by graphical means. Produce the straight part of the curve, then for a particular temperature the part of the ordinate P_r between the straight line and the curve is proportional to the radiation loss.

Thus $\quad P_r = k_2 T^n$

Note: We can neglect the term $k_2 T_0^n$, because it is relatively small.

6 Plot a graph with lg (P_r/W) on the y-axis and lg (T/K) on the x-axis, and use it to determine the value of n.

7 Comment on the assumptions that have been made in this experiment.

Answers

Chapter 1

1.1 (a) The zeroth law states that two systems, A and B, which are each in thermal equilibrium with a third system, C, must be in thermal equilibrium with each other. C could be a thermometer. If it reads the same when in thermal equilibrium with A *or* B then A *and* B are at the same temperature and must be in thermal equilibrium with each other.
(b) Yes; energy is transferred from the hot sun to your cooler body by radiation.
(c) Unlikely; thermal equilibrium between two systems implies equal temperatures. A thermometer could be used to verify the answer.

1.3 (a) The triple point of water is that unique temperature and pressure at which there is equilibrium between the solid, liquid and vapour phases for water (273.16 K, 608.6 Pa).
(b) 352 K.

1.4 (a) A temperature scale is defined by a particular property of one material and there is no reason why two temperature scales should agree (except at the fixed points). A mercury thermometer will record 79 °C for the boiling point if the change in the length of the mercury column between the ice point and the normal b.p. of alcohol is 0.79 of the change between 0 °C and 100 °C. Other properties will change by a different fraction and record a different temperature for the normal b.p.
(b) See figure 1.9, in which $\Delta\theta$ is the difference between the temperatures recorded on the thermocouple and resistance scales. The values of temperatures on the thermocouple scale for temperatures of 25 °C, 50 °C and 75 °C on the platinum resistance scale are 24.1 °C, 48.9 °C and 74.4 °C respectively.

1.5 $T = 273.16\,\text{K}\left(\dfrac{p_T}{p_{\text{tr}}}\right)$

1.6 The kelvin is the fraction 1/273.16 of the thermodynamic temperature of the triple point of water. The interval between the ice and steam points is not defined as 100 K. On the best available experimental evidence it is 100 K, but it is possible that future evidence could change this.

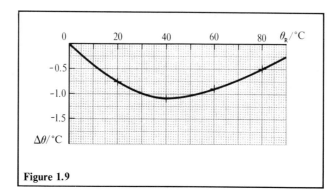

Figure 1.9

1.7 (a) The volume of mercury must increase uniformly with temperature on a mercury-in-glass scale (neglecting the effect of the glass expansion) because of the way a temperature scale is defined. However, mercury does not expand uniformly with temperature recorded on other temperature scales.
(b) Temperature would have to be measured on the thermodynamic scale using a standard thermometer whose readings could be corrected to the thermodynamic scale. The value of the varying physical property of a body must be measured when the body is in thermal equilibrium with the thermometer. It would be necessary to ensure that the whole body was at this equilibrium temperature. A graph of $X/(\text{unit})$ against T/K could then be obtained.

1.8 Bi-metal spiral coils are used to measure temperature.

1.9 (a) $\alpha = \dfrac{\text{fractional increase in length}}{\text{temperature rise}} = \dfrac{\Delta l/l_0}{\Delta\theta}$.
(b) For expansion from 0 °C to θ,
$\Delta l = l_\theta - l_0 = l_0\ \theta$,
so $l_\theta = l_0(1 + \alpha\theta)$.
In this equation α is the average linear expansivity in the temperature range 0 °C to θ.
(c) (i) α is not constant, it depends on the temperature range.
(ii) α is independent of direction in the material in isotropic substances (e.g. non-crystalline metals). α depends on direction in anisotropic substances (e.g. crystals).

1.10 (a) 1.2×10^{-4} m.
(b) 1.2×10^3 N; $F = EA\alpha\theta$.

1.12 (a) For an ideal gas $V \propto T$ (where T is the temperature on the thermodynamic scale). For an ideal gas expanding from V_0 to V_{100}, between the ice and steam points,
$$\frac{V_{100}}{V_0} = \frac{373.15}{273.15} = \left(1 + \frac{100}{273.15}\right)$$
But $\dfrac{V_{100}}{V_0} = (1 + 100\alpha_l)$

Thus the volume coefficient of an ideal gas = $1/273.15$ K^{-1}. Temperature scales based on real gases for which α is near to $1/273.15$ K^{-1} will agree closely with the ideal gas scale, and therefore with the thermodynamic scale.
(b) If a constant volume hydrogen scale agrees with an ideal gas scale,
$$p_\theta = p_0\left(1 + \frac{\theta}{273.15}\right),$$
where θ is the temperature measured on the Celsius thermodynamic scale. The value of β is $1/273.15$ K^{-1}.

1.13 (a) When the temperature of a metal is raised, the thermal vibrations of the atoms increase. The free electrons are thus likely to make more collisions per unit time, so the drift velocity will decrease. Thus the resistance of the metal increases.
(b) In an intrinsic semiconductor, an increase in temperature causes an increase in thermal agitation. As a result, electrons are freed from the parent atoms and positive holes are created. The increase in available charge carriers (electrons and positive holes) decreases the resistance.

1.14 (a) $R_{100} = R_0(1 + 4 \times 10^{-1} - 6 \times 10^{-3})$
$\qquad\qquad = R_0(1.394)$
(b) $R_{60} = R_0(1.238)$
$\theta_{\text{Pt}} = \dfrac{(R_{60} - R_0)}{(R_{100} - R_0)} \times 100 = \dfrac{23.8}{0.394} = 60.4\ °\text{C}$

1.15 The platinum resistance scale will be in closest agreement with the ideal gas scale, because α_{Pt} is closest to $\alpha_{ideal\ gas}$ (3.66×10^{-3} K^{-1} or 1/273 K^{-1}).

1.16 (a) β is negative.
(b) For the temperature difference range -50 K to $+150$ K (50 K below the reference temperature to 150 K above), that is, for the part of the graph which is approximately linear.
(c) (i) Ice point, (ii) m.p. zinc (692.73 K) or m.p. lead (600 K).
(d) First measure the e.m.f. for a known temperature difference when both junctions are at known temperatures (e.g. E_{100} for junctions at 0 °C and 100 °C). Then measure the e.m.f. for the unknown temperature difference, when the reference junction is at a known temperature and the other junction at the unknown temperature (e.g. E_θ for 0 °C and θ). The unknown temperature θ is given by

$$\frac{\theta}{100} = \frac{E_\theta}{E_{100}}.$$

1.17 (a) Temperature is 19.5 °C on a water vapour pressure scale when $\theta = 60$ °C on the Celsius thermodynamic scale.
(b) See figure 1.10.
(c) (i) Temperature on lg p scale = 68 °C, (1.52/2.22 × 100 °C)
(ii) Temperature on lg p scale = 89 °C.
The graph of lg p against θ is more linear than the graph of p against θ. The lg p temperature scale is in closer agreement than the p scale with the Celsius thermodynamic scale.

1.19 (a) Radiation pyrometer – suitable for temperatures beyond 1750 K.
(b) Mercury-in-glass (clinical) – cheap, convenient.
(c) Constant volume gas – accurate.
(d) Constant volume gas, thermoelectric and electrical resistance thermometers are all suitable for low temperatures.
(e) Thermoelectric and electrical resistance thermometers provide remote probes.

1.20 (b) Platinum resistance thermometer. An agreed formula is required relating the resistance of platinum with temperature on the I.P.T.S.

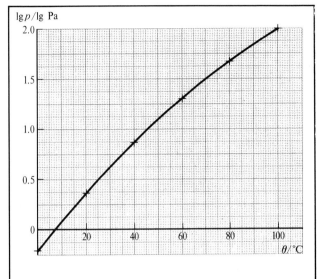

Figure 1.10

Chapter 2

2.1 *Heat* is energy which is transferred as a result of a temperature difference.
Energy is the capacity for doing work.
Internal energy is the energy possessed by the particles of matter due to their motion (kinetic energy), or due to their arrangement or separation (potential energy stored in the system due to intermolecular forces).

2.3 (a) The joule, symbol J.
(b) 2.4×10^4 J.
$Q = (2.0$ kg$)(4.0 \times 10^2$ J kg^{-1} K$^{-1})(30$ K$)$.
(c) 14.5 m s^{-1}.
$\frac{1}{2} \times 0.50$ kg $\times v^2 \times 75/100 = (2 \times 4.0 \times 10^2 \times 0.05)$ J, where v is the speed of the hammer.

2.4 (a) Heat is required to increase the temperature of the pipes (also, initially, the water in the pipes between the tap and the hot water cistern is cold!).
(b) 1.7×10^5 J.
Mass of copper pipe
$$= (9.0 \times 10^3 \text{ kg m}^{-3})(4.0 \text{ m})(3.0 \times 10^{-4} \text{ m}^2)$$
$$= 10.8 \text{ kg}$$
$Q = (10.8$ kg$)(4.0 \times 10^2$ J kg^{-1} K$^{-1})(40$ K$)$
$= 1.7 \times 10^5$ J

2.5 (a) 11.8 A.
$$\frac{\text{electrical energy}}{\text{transformed}} = \frac{\text{heat received}}{\text{by tank}} + \frac{\text{heat received}}{\text{by water}}$$

$$I \times 240 \text{ V} \times (30 \times 60 \text{ s}) = (2.0 \times 4.0 \times 10^2 \times 60) \text{ J}$$
$$+ (20 \times 4.2 \times 10^2 \times 60) \text{ J}$$

(b) Data required:
dimensions of bath 2 m × 0.5 m × 0.3 m,
density of water 1.0×10^3 kg m^{-3},
initial temperature 15 °C,
final temperature 45 °C,
cost of unit of electricity 3p per kilowatt hour,
Estimate: about 10 kW hr, costing 30 pence.

2.6 The specific heat capacity of copper does not have a constant value – it increases as the temperature increases. The variation between 273 K and 373 K is comparatively small (c is usually assumed to be constant in this range), but the value decreases rapidly with decreasing temperature below this range.

2.7 For liquids and solids it would be very difficult to increase the pressure sufficiently to keep the volume constant.

2.8

Element	$C_p M_m$/J mol^{-1} K^{-1}
aluminium	23.7
copper	24.2
lead	26.2
sodium	27.2

The molar heat capacity is very nearly the same for all these substances (this result was first discovered by Dulong and Petit). In fact, providing the temperature is high enough, it takes just as much energy to raise the temperature of 1 mole of aluminium by 1 K as it does to raise the temperature of 1 mole of copper by 1 K, despite the different masses. The same amount of energy is needed per molecule.

2.9 (a) The solid line in figure 2.7 is the graph of the results. Specific heat capacity of aluminium is 1.2×10^3 J kg^{-1} K^{-1}. The rise in temperature of the aluminium block is 12.5 °C, so 60 W × 500 s = 2.0 kg × c × 12.5 K
where c is the specific heat capacity of aluminium.
(b) It will have no effect (providing the block is at room temperature at the start of the experiment).
(c) It takes a certain amount of time for the heat to be conducted through the aluminium, hence the relatively slow rise in the first 100 s. Heat is still being conducted through the block after the heater is switched off, hence the temperature continues to rise for a while. The reading begins to fall after about 600 s because the aluminium block continues to transfer heat to the surroundings.
(d) Higher. The aluminium block loses energy to the surroundings. If this did not happen, the rise in temperature would be higher, thus the specific heat capacity would be a lower value.

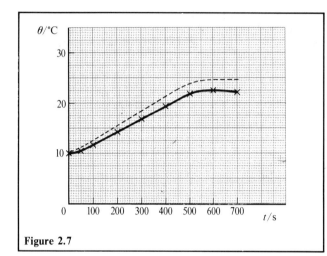

Figure 2.7

(e) Surround the aluminium block with an insulating material, such as cotton wool. The curve you might then obtain is shown by the dotted line in figure 2.7. The curve has a steeper slope initially, reaches a higher maximum temperature, and thereafter the temperature falls more slowly than with an unlagged block. This is because more of the energy supplied by the heater is retained in the block during the period of the experiment and the rate of loss of heat to the surroundings is reduced.

2.12 1.7×10^3 J kg^{-1} K^{-1}.

electrical energy transformed	= energy required to increase temperature of liquid	+ energy lost to surroundings

1st experiment:
3.0 A × 12 V × 60 s = 420×10^{-3} kg × c × 4.0 K + Q_1

2nd experiment:
2.5 A × 10 V × 120 s = 650×10^{-3} kg × c × 4.0 K + Q_2

where c is the specific heat capacity of the liquid, Q_1 is the energy lost to the surroundings in 60 s and Q_2 is the energy lost in 120 s. Since the excess temperature is the same in the two experiments, $Q_2 = 2 Q_1$.

2.14 During the heating part of the experiment, the average excess temperature is roughly half that during the cooling part. Thus, the average heat loss during the heating part is roughly equal to the average heat loss in the cooling part (i.e. in half the time).

2.16 (a) The rate at which energy was being transferred from the heating coil to the oil was equal to the rate at which the calorimeter was transferring energy to the surroundings.
(b)

Rate of loss of energy P/W	3.8	6.2	9.4	19.0	33.6
Excess temperature $(\theta - \theta_0)$/°C	21.0	30.0	42.0	74.0	117.0

The graph (figure 2.8) is approximately linear, showing that the rate of loss of energy is proportional to the excess temperature.

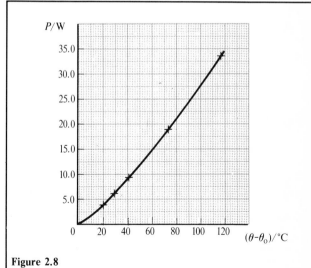

Figure 2.8

2.17 Assume that the conditions are such that the rate of loss of heat is proportional to excess temperature:

rate of loss of heat = $k A (\theta - \theta_0)$

rate of loss of heat = $m c \times$ rate of fall of temperature

rate of fall of temperature = $k A (\theta - \theta_0) / m c$.

The mass of a body is proportional to its volume, thus the rate of fall of temperature of a body is proportional to the ratio of its surface area to its volume, that is, it is inversely proportional to a linear dimension. It follows that a smaller body cools faster than a large one.

2.18 (a) (i) From A to B the temperature of the solid was increasing, but it remained solid. (ii) From B to C the solid was changing into a liquid; it began to melt. There was a change of phase, from solid phase to liquid phase. (iii) From C to D the temperature of the liquid was increasing. (iv) From D to E another change of phase was taking place, from the liquid phase to the gaseous phase. That is, the liquid was boiling. (b) The energy was being used to change the phase of the substance (see chapter 3).

2.20 (a) 1.65×10^6 J.

Energy required = $(5.0 \text{ kg}) (3.3 \times 10^5 \text{ J kg}^{-1})$

(b) 78.6 °C.

$1.65 \times 10^6 \text{ J} = (5.0 \text{ kg}) (4.2 \times 10^3 \text{ J kg}^{-1} \text{ K}^{-1}) \times \theta$,

where θ is the increase in temperature.

2.21 (a) Water is used because it has a high specific heat capacity compared to other substances, so for a given heat transfer the rise in temperature would be less. With an air-cooled engine the main problem is arranging for the heat to be dissipated. In terms of volume, approximately 4000 times more air than water must pass through an engine to dissipate an equal quantity of heat. In small air-cooled engines, the cooling fins add no more bulk than water cooling jackets. A multi-cylinder engine, however, requires a large fan as well as larger fins or a cowling to direct air to the hot sections of the engine.

(b) 1.32×10^7 J.

energy required = $\dfrac{\text{energy to increase}}{\text{temperature}} + \dfrac{\text{energy to change}}{\text{phase}}$

$Q = (5.0 \text{ kg}) (4.2 \times 10^3 \text{ J kg}^{-1} \text{ K}^{-1}) (80 \text{ K})$
$\quad + (5.0 \text{ kg}) (2.3 \times 10^6 \text{ J kg}^{-1})$

2.22 8.0×10^5 J kg^{-1}, 2 W.

$(3.0 \text{ A}) (10.0 \text{ V}) (200 \text{ s}) = (7.0 \times 10^{-3} \text{ kg}) l + Q$

$(4.0 \text{ A}) (12.5 \text{ V}) (200 \text{ s}) = (12.0 \times 10^{-3} \text{ kg}) l + Q$

where Q is the energy lost to the surroundings in 200 s.

2.24 1.69×10^{-2} kg.

Let m be the mass of nitrogen vaporised, then energy required to change the phase of the nitrogen is m $(2.5 \times 10^5 \text{ J kg}^{-1})$. Heat transferred resulting from change in internal energy of the water and ice:

water from 20 °C to 0 °C
$\quad = (0.005 \text{ kg}) (4.2 \times 10^3 \text{ J kg}^{-1} \text{ K}^{-1}) (20 \text{ K})$;

water to ice at 0 °C = $(0.005 \text{ kg}) (3.3 \times 10^5 \text{ J kg}^{-1})$;

ice from 0 °C to -196 °C
$\quad = (0.005 \text{ kg}) (2.2 \times 10^3 \text{ J kg}^{-1} \text{ K}^{-1}) (196 \text{ K})$.

2.25

Power to increase temperature
$\quad = (0.04 \text{ kg s}^{-1}) (4.2 \times 10^3 \text{ J kg}^{-1} \text{ K}^{-1}) (73 \text{ K})$,

power to change phase = $(0.04 \text{ kg s}^{-1}) (2.3 \times 10^6 \text{ J kg}^{-1})$,

10.4×10^4 W will be required to produce 0.04 kg of steam every second.

Reflector	Power/10⁴ W
A	2.6
B	7.8
C	13.0
D	15.6

For reflector A, the power available is given by

$(1.35 \times 10^3 \text{ W m}^{-2}) \left(\dfrac{95}{100} \right) (20 \text{ m}^2)$.

Consider the energy losses from the boilers and find which combinations will have available at least 10.4×10^4 W. This gives the following combinations:

C with G (not quite) or H,

D with E, F, G or H.

The cheapest combinations are C with G and D with E (both cost £1100).

Chapter 3

3.1 (a) Yes. For an ideal gas pV is constant, so the gas pressure will decrease to enable V to be as large as any container. There is no attractive force between the molecules of an ideal gas so there is nothing to prevent it from expanding to fill any volume.

(b) No. An ideal gas is always compressible (if p increases, V must decrease), and this is not true for a liquid. There are forces of attraction between molecules in a liquid, but no forces of attraction between molecules in an ideal gas.

3.3 No. Faster bodies tend to slow down and slower bodies to gain kinetic energy, though some collisions do occur in which a fast body is speeded up and a slow one loses speed. In an elastic head-on collision with a stationary body of equal mass, all the energy is transferred. In oblique collisions only part of the energy is transferred. On average, in atomic collisions, half of the kinetic energy is transferred.

3.4 No. Some molecules will, momentarily, have more than average energy, some less. The collision process will produce frequent changes in the speeds of individual molecules but the distribution of speeds will be unchanged.

3.5 (a) 2.25×10^3 m s^{-1}.

(b) Total k.e. = $\frac{1}{2} m \{ (2 \times 1^2) + (3 \times 2^2)$
$\qquad + (2 \times 3^2) + (1 \times 4^2) \} \times 10^6 \text{ m}^2 \text{ s}^{-2}$
$\qquad = 24 m \times 10^6 \text{ m}^2 \text{ s}^{-2}$

(c) $\sqrt{6} \times 10^3$ m s^{-1}.

If v is the unknown speed,

$\frac{1}{2} \times 8 m v^2 = 24 m \times 10^6 \text{ m}^2 \text{ s}^{-2}$

(e) $\sqrt{\dfrac{N_1 c_1^2 + N_2 c_2^2 + \cdots + N_r c_r^2}{N_1 + N_2 + \cdots + N_r}}$

3.6 (a) $PN = r \cos \theta$.

(b) $PQ = 2r \cos \theta$.

(c) $QR = 2r \cos \theta$.

(d) Time taken $= \dfrac{2r \cos \theta}{c_1}$

(e) $\dfrac{c_1}{2r \cos \theta}$ collisions per second.

(f) $\dfrac{N_1 c_1 t}{2r \cos \theta}$

(g) $\dfrac{N_1 c_1 t}{2r \cos \theta} \cdot \dfrac{A}{4\pi r^2}$ collisions on A in time t.

(h) Momentum change per collision $= 2mc_1 \cos \theta$.

(i) $F =$ change in momentum per second
$=$ number of collisions per second $\times$ change in
momentum per collision.

$$F = \frac{N_1 c_1}{2r \cos \theta} \cdot \frac{A}{4\pi r^2} \cdot 2 m c_1 \cos \theta,$$

$$F = \frac{m N_1 c_1^2 A}{4\pi r^3}.$$

(Notice that this force does not depend on θ, only the speed matters.)

(j) $p = \dfrac{F}{A} = \dfrac{m N_1 c_1^2}{4\pi r^3}$

(k) $p = \dfrac{m N}{4\pi r^3} \left(\dfrac{N_1 c_1^2 + N_2 c_2^2 + \cdots}{N} \right)$

$= \dfrac{\frac{1}{3} m N \overline{c^2}}{\frac{4}{3} \pi r^3} = \dfrac{\frac{1}{3} m N \overline{c^2}}{V}$

3.8 (a) $\sqrt{\overline{c^2}} = \sqrt{\dfrac{3 \times 10^5 \text{ Pa}}{1.29 \text{ kg m}^{-3}}} = 482$ m s^{-1}

(b) $\rho_{373} = \left(1.29 \times \dfrac{273}{373} \right)$ kg m^{-3}, $\sqrt{\overline{c^2}} = 563$ m s^{-1}

(c) $\sqrt{\overline{c^2}} = \sqrt{\dfrac{3 \times 10^5 \text{ Pa}}{9 \times 10^{-2} \text{ kg m}^{-3}}}$

$= \sqrt{\left(\dfrac{10^7}{3} \right)}$ m s^{-1} $= 1.83 \times 10^3$ m s^{-1}

3.9 The speed of sound is greater in hydrogen because the molecular speeds are greater in hydrogen. Also hydrogen is less dense, and the speed of sound is inversely proportional to the square root of the density of the gas.

3.10 (i) p is the most probable speed, because it is at the peak of the curve. The number of molecules in any small range of speeds is greatest for speeds around p.
(ii) q must be the mean speed. The areas under the curve are equal on either side of the mean.

3.12 (a) Increases.
(b) Increases.
(c) Decreases.

3.13 At the same temperature,
$\frac{1}{2} m_H \overline{c_H^2} = \frac{1}{2} m_O \overline{c_O^2}$
$m_H/m_O = 1/16$, therefore $\overline{c_H^2}/\overline{c_O^2} = 16/1$
and $\sqrt{\overline{c_H^2}}/\sqrt{\overline{c_O^2}} = 4/1$.

3.14 (a) $pV = \frac{1}{3} m_1 N_1 \overline{c_1^2} = \frac{1}{3} m_2 N_2 \overline{c_2^2}$
(b) $\frac{1}{2} m_1 \overline{c_1^2} = \frac{1}{2} m_2 \overline{c_2^2}$.
(c) $N_1 = N_2$. The two gases contain equal numbers of molecules.

3.15 (a) $pV = \dfrac{N}{N_A} RT$.

(b) $pV = \frac{1}{3} m N \overline{c^2}$.

(c) $pV = \left(\frac{2}{3} N \right) \left(\frac{1}{2} m \overline{c^2} \right) = \frac{2}{3} N \times \frac{3}{2} kT = NkT$

3.16 (a) 1 mole contains N_A molecules.

Average k.e. of a molecule $= \frac{3}{2} kT$.

Total translational k.e. per mole $= \frac{3}{2} k N_A T = \frac{3}{2} RT$.

This is the same for all gases.
(b) Molar mass $M_m = m N_A$.

But $\frac{1}{2} m N_A \overline{c^2} = \frac{3}{2} RT$, from part (a),

so $\overline{c^2} = \dfrac{3RT}{M_m}$, $\sqrt{(\overline{c^2})} = c_{\text{r.m.s.}} = \sqrt{\dfrac{3RT}{M_m}}$

$M_m = 0.002$ kg mol^{-1},
$c_{\text{r.m.s.}} = 1.8 \times 10^3$ m s^{-1}.

3.17 (a) $k = R/N_A = \dfrac{8.3 \text{ J mol}^{-1} \text{ K}^{-1}}{6 \times 10^{23} \text{ mol}^{-1}}$

$= 1.38 \times 10^{-23}$ J K^{-1}

average k.e. $= \frac{3}{2} kT = 6.2 \times 10^{-21}$ J

(b) Yes.
(c) $m = 5.0 \times 10^{-26}$ kg.
$\frac{1}{2} m \overline{c^2} = \frac{3}{2} kT$,

$m = \dfrac{2 \times 6.2 \times 10^{-21} \text{ J}}{500^2 \text{ m}^2 \text{ s}^{-2}}$

3.21 (a) r.m.s. speed $= \sqrt{3 \times 10^5\,\text{Pa}/7.5\,\text{kg m}^{-3}} = 200\,\text{m s}^{-1}$.
(b) 10^5 m.
(c) $\lambda N = 10^5$ m.
(d) $\lambda \sqrt{N} = 0.1$ m.
(e) $\lambda N/\lambda\sqrt{N} = \sqrt{N} = 10^6$, so $N = 10^{12}$.
Therefore $\lambda = 10^5\,\text{m}/10^{12} = 10^{-7}$ m.

3.23 (a) Layer A.
(b) Momentum is transferred from A to B by molecules moving across the boundary.
(c) Near the boundary layer A will tend to slow down; B will tend to speed up.

3.24 (a) Force $\propto$ area, because number of molecules transferring momentum will be proportional to area of boundary.
(b) Viscous force will increase as the velocity difference increases, since the rate at which momentum is transferred depends on velocity difference.

3.27 (a) pA.
(b) Work done $= pA\,\delta x = p\delta V$.
(c) $p\delta V$ has units $\text{N m}^{-2} \times \text{m}^3$ or Nm or J.
(d) Pressure is constant.
(e) By the area of a rectangle, CABD in figure 3.11, of width δV, length p.
(f) By the area of a strip of width δV *under* the curve.
(g) (i) By the total area under the curve between V_1 and V_2.
(ii) By a rectangle, AEGC, of area $p(V_2 - V_1)$.

3.28 (a) $W_1 > W_2$. The gas does more external work in change 1.
(b) $\Delta U_1 = \Delta U_2$.
(c) Since $Q = W + \Delta U$, $Q_1 > Q_2$. More heat is transferred into the gas in change 1 than in change 2.

3.29 A reversible process is a theoretical ideal. It is a change which occurs in such a way that the system is always in thermodynamic equilibrium (no temperature or pressure gradients). It must be an infinitely slow process and the system can be thought of as passing through an infinite series of equilibrium states. An infinitely small change in the controlling conditions will reverse the process (e.g. an infinitely small change in the force acting on a piston of a gas cylinder will change expansion to contraction).
In a reversible change, there must be no work done against friction producing changes in internal energy (this energy change cannot be reversed).

3.30 $pV = $ constant.

3.32 Work is done on the gas to compress it. This will produce an increase in internal energy and therefore the temperature will rise.

3.33 Isothermal change must occur infinitely slowly in a perfectly conducting container, otherwise there will be some temperature change. Adiabatic change must be instantaneous or in a perfectly lagged container – again an impossibility.

3.34 The expansion is almost adiabatic, resulting in cooling of the expanding air.

3.35 (a) Boyle's law.
(b) pV/T is constant.
(c) p/T is constant.
(d) 150 K and 450 K.
(e) BE_2, because cooling occurs during adiabatic expansion.
(f) From the graph (point B):

$$\frac{pV}{T} = \frac{2 \times 10^5\,\text{Pa} \times 10^{-3}\text{m}^3}{300\,\text{K}} = \frac{2}{3}\,\text{J K}^{-1}$$

For a mass M of gas,
$pV/T = MR/M_m$,
where M_m is the molar mass ($3.2 \times 10^{-2}\,\text{kg mol}^{-1}$).
Therefore $M = \dfrac{M_m}{R}\left(\dfrac{pV}{T}\right)$

$$M = \frac{3.2 \times 10^{-2}\,\text{kg mol}^{-1}}{8.3\,\text{J mol}^{-1}\,\text{K}^{-1}} \times \frac{2}{3}\,\text{J K}^{-1} = 2.57 \times 10^{-3}\,\text{kg}.$$

(g) Energy needed $= p\delta V = 10^5\,\text{Pa} \times 10^{-3}\,\text{m}^3 = 100$ J.

3.37 See figure 3.14. The area under the isothermal is greater than the area under the adiabatic.

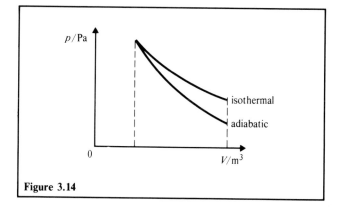

Figure 3.14

3.38 (a) $T_2 = 227$ K

$$T_2 = T_1 \left(\frac{V_1}{V_2}\right)^{\gamma-1} = 300\,(\tfrac{1}{2})^{0.4}\ \text{K}$$

$$\lg(T_2/\text{K}) = \lg 300 - 0.4\,\lg 2$$

(b) $p_2 = 3.79 \times 10^4$ Pa.

$$p_2 = p_1 \left(\frac{V_1}{V_2}\right)\left(\frac{T_2}{T_1}\right) = 10^5\ \text{Pa}\left(\frac{1}{2}\right)\left(\frac{227}{300}\right)$$

3.39 (a) The molar heat capacity at constant volume, C_V, is the heat required to produce unit rise in temperature in one mole of the gas when the volume is kept constant. The unit of C_V is J mol^{-1} K^{-1}.

(b) $Q = n\,C_V\,\Delta T$

(c) $\Delta U = n\,C_V\,\Delta T$

3.40 (a) (i) $\frac{3}{2}nRT$, (ii) $\frac{3}{2}nR\,(T + \Delta T)$.

(b) Change in k.e. $= \frac{3}{2}nR\,\Delta T$.

(c) $\Delta U = \frac{3}{2}nR\Delta T = n\,C_V\Delta T$,

$$C_V = \frac{3}{2}R.$$

(d) 12 J mol^{-1} K^{-1}, which agrees closely with the data given for the monatomic gases He, Ar, Ne.

3.41 (a) $Q = n\,C_p\,\Delta T$

$\Delta U = n\,C_V\,\Delta T$

(b) $Q = \Delta U + W$

$n C_p \Delta T = n C_V \Delta T + W$

(c) $C_p - C_V = \dfrac{W}{n\,\Delta T}$

Chapter 4

4.1 See figure 4.14.

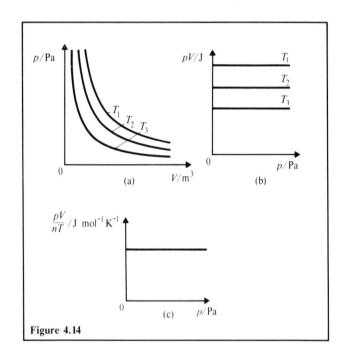
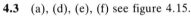

Figure 4.14

4.3 (a), (d), (e), (f) see figure 4.15.

(b) This is a region of the graph where the isothermals are almost vertical, indicating a very small decrease in volume for a large increase in pressure. This is a characteristic property of a liquid.

(c) In the shaded region vapour and liquid coexist in equilibrium. Between A and B the volume increases, as an increasing proportion of the substance vaporises.

(g) Heat must be supplied when the CO_2 changes from state A to state B because (i) the carbon dioxide does work in expanding at constant pressure, and (ii) energy is required to evaporate the liquid.

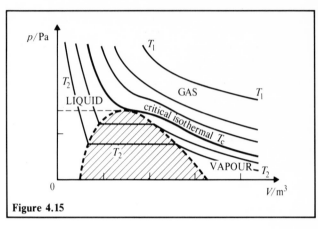

Figure 4.15

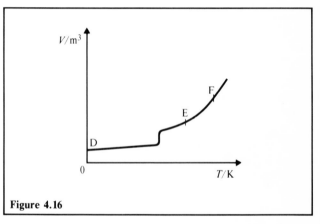

Figure 4.16

4.4 (a) See figure 4.16. (i) The solid substance expands when the temperature is raised. (ii) Its volume increases on melting. (iii) At E the substance is described as liquid (because its temperature is below the critical temperature), and at F it is described as a gas. However, the compressibility and density of the substance change little between E and F; there are no sudden changes in properties.

(b) Below T_{tr}, as the pressure increases the substance changes from vapour to solid (without any intervening liquid phase).

4.5 (a) (i) T and p are constant, (ii) V varies as the nitrogen undergoes a transition between gas and liquid phases. Between A and B nitrogen is a liquid; V is constant and pV/n changes steadily with p.
(b) At 126 K the nitrogen remains at constant pressure for a range of different volumes as vapour and liquid exist in equilibrium. 126 K must be below T_c. There is no vertical part to the graph at 151 K, so this must be above T_c.
(c) At 379 K, pV/n for nitrogen is greater than for the ideal gas (pV/n for an ideal gas equals pV/n for nitrogen at zero pressure). At 252 K, pV/n for nitrogen is less than for the ideal gas at pressures below 2×10^7 Pa. The Boyle temperature will be between 379 K and 252 K.

4.6 (a) No, under no conditions, because 0 °C is above the critical temperature for oxygen.
(b) Yes. Although the normal boiling point of carbon dioxide is higher than -90 °C, it can boil at a lower temperature if the pressure is reduced.

4.7 (a) $Q = 0$, $W = 0$.
(b) Since $\Delta U = Q - W$, $\Delta U = 0$.
(c) The internal energy is contained in the kinetic and potential energy of the molecules. If the potential energy of the molecules increases, the kinetic energy must decrease by an equal amount, producing a cooling of the gas.

4.8 The thermal capacity of the water bath is very much larger than that of the gas. Any cooling of the gas would cause a fall in the temperature of the water too small to detect.

4.11 It must be cooled below its critical temperature.

4.15 (a) Heat is required to evaporate a liquid, so energy is used in separating molecules against attractive forces. Surface tension also provides evidence of intermolecular attraction.
(b) Kinetic energy due to random motion, and potential energy which depends on their separation and the intermolecular forces.
(c) It must be travelling away from the liquid surface towards the gas and have enough kinetic energy to supply the energy to do work against the molecular attraction forces.
(d) As the temperature rises a greater proportion of the molecules in the liquid will have a speed greater than the minimum speed required to escape, and so rate of escape will increase as temperature rises.

4.16 The theory suggests that there is a steady escape of the faster molecules, so the average molecular kinetic energy in the liquid will decrease, and the temperature will fall.

4.17 (i) Yes. Vibrating molecules of a solid may acquire enough kinetic energy to escape.
(ii) Yes. Even at low temperatures random processes will produce some high speed molecules.
Crystalline solid 'air fresheners' evaporate. So does snow. On a cold dry day wet washing hung on the line may freeze and still evaporate until dry.

4.18 (a) When a substance melts, relatively few molecular bonds are broken. When evaporation occurs, all the remaining bonds must be broken.
(b) See figure 4.17. Suppose at 50 °C the molecular separation varies from A to A', then at 100 °C it could vary from B to B' with greater amplitude, producing greater average separation at 100 °C. Since the average separation is increased, less energy is required at 100 °C to break the molecular bond. The graph shows how the energy $E_{p,T}$ needed to escape decreases with temperature.
(c) 6.8×10^{-20} J.

$$\text{Energy required} = \frac{2260 \text{ kJ kg}^{-1} \times 0.018 \text{ kg mol}^{-1}}{6 \times 10^{23} \text{ mol}^{-1}}$$

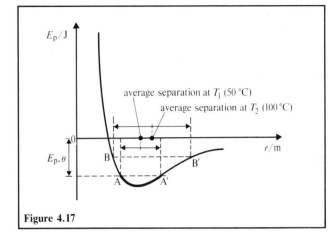

Figure 4.17

4.19 (a) The mercury column records atmospheric pressure.
(b) A small quantity of liquid is introduced and evaporates into the space above the mercury. The pressure of this vapour lowers the level of the mercury meniscus.
(c) More liquid is introduced and evaporates. The increasing density of the vapour produces a greater vapour pressure, further reducing the height of the column of mercury. Sufficient liquid has now been introduced for a layer of liquid to form on the top of the mercury column. Molecules leave the liquid and evaporate into the space, but molecules also return to the liquid. When the rates of evaporation and condensation are equal, the pressure exerted by the vapour becomes constant. The liquid and vapour are in dynamic equilibrium and the vapour is a saturated vapour. Introducing more liquid will not increase the pressure.
(d) If the tube is tilted the volume occupied by the vapour is decreased but the height of the mercury column is unchanged. Some of the vapour in (c) must have condensed, since the pressure of the saturated vapour is unchanged.

4.20 Increasing the temperature increases the average kinetic energy of the molecules and increases the rate of escape. More molecules will leave than are returning, the vapour will become more dense until at a certain density the rate of return balances the rate of escape. At higher temperatures a saturated vapour is more dense and contains faster molecules: both factors will increase the pressure it exerts.

4.21 (a) Increasing the volume reduces the vapour density, so the number of molecules escaping exceeds the number returning until a new equilibrium is established, with the vapour density and pressure unaffected by increase in volume. If the volume is decreased, the vapour density is temporarily increased, so the rate of return exceeds the rate of escape until equilibrium is established at a density and pressure unchanged by the decrease in volume. The presence of other molecules does not affect the dynamic equilibrium between a vapour and its liquid.
(b) The space becomes supersaturated. The rate of return exceeds the rate of escape. The pressure of the saturated vapour decreases because the vapour density decreases and the r.m.s. speed of the vapour molecules decreases.
(c) See figure 4.18.

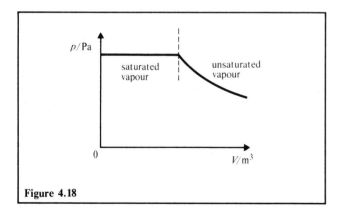

Figure 4.18

4.22 (a) The carbon dioxide is below its critical temperature and vapour and liquid exist in equilibrium.
(b) The pressure exerted is the s.v.p. for carbon dioxide at that temperature, and will not change as long as some liquid remains in the cylinder.

4.23 The s.v.p. equals the external pressure if the liquid is boiling. Reducing the external pressure lowers the boiling point, because boiling can now occur at a temperature at which the s.v.p. equals the reduced pressure.

4.24 (a) (i) To expel the air. (ii) The pressure-cooker contains saturated vapour and little evaporation occurs; just enough to replace vapour escaping from the pressure valve. (iii) The food is raised to a higher temperature in a pressure-cooker than in water boiling at normal atmospheric pressure.
(b) Approximately 121 °C in this case.

4.25 The pressure inside the liquid at the bottom is greater than that at the surface. The liquid will only boil at the bottom when the s.v.p. equals the pressure in the liquid at this point, which is greater than atmospheric pressure.

4.26 Bubble diameter = 2×10^{-8} m,
$$p = \frac{2 \times 2.5 \times 10^{-2} \, \text{N m}^{-1}}{10^{-8} \, \text{m}}$$
$$= 5 \times 10^{6} \, \text{N m}^{-2} \approx 50 \text{ atmospheres.}$$

4.27 There are no nuclei (empty spaces into which the liquid can evaporate) for forming bubbles, because gentle heating has removed air bubbles, pure water contains no solid particles, and the round-bottomed flask has no rough surfaces. The water will become superheated.
This is a situation of unstable equilibrium. Any stirring of the water or vibration of the bench will produce sudden boiling. Reducing the pressure will increase the instability and sudden violent boiling (bumping) will probably occur as bubbles form rapidly around any tiny air spaces in the water.

4.28 Air pressure at 20 °C = $(100 - 2.2)$ kPa = 97.8 kPa.
Air pressure at 100 °C = $97.8 \times \dfrac{373}{293}$ kPa = 133.6 kPa.
Pressure of saturated water vapour at 100 °C = 100 kPa.
Total pressure = 233.6 kPa.
The water will not boil because water only boils at 100 °C if the pressure is 100 kPa.

4.29 The air expands and cools as it rises and the vapour present is sufficent to saturate the air at the lower temperature.

4.31 (a) Adiabatic expansion; temperature decrease.
(b) There is a steady temperature gradient in the chamber. The lower layers of air and vapour are cooler than the upper layers. Saturated vapour in the upper layers diffuses downwards, becoming supersaturated, and may condense on the base. It acts continuously because the chamber provides a continuous source of supersaturated vapour.
(c) The plastic top is charged to remove any ions from the chamber. Drops will then form only on the new ions along the track of the emitted radiation.

4.32 (a) Near the boiling point.
(b) The liquid becomes superheated (i.e. it is at a temperature above the boiling point).
(c) A liquid is more dense than a gas, so more collisions occur and more ions are formed in unit length of track.

Chapter 5

5.2 (a) Because it collects the heat from the device, and is designed in such a way that it enables a rapid transfer of heat to the surroundings to take place.

(b) Connected in such a way as to allow a maximum rate of transfer of heat (by conduction).

(c) You should have mentioned conduction from the device to the heat sink, conduction through the metal and convection to the surrounding air.

(d) You should have referred to surface area: by having fins, a larger surface area is in contact with the air.

(e) Vertically. This will allow air to move freely over the surface. If placed horizontally, air would be trapped.

(f) A watt is a unit of power, and is equal to 1 joule per second. The statement means that, at an excess temperature of 30 °C, energy is being transferred to the surroundings at the rate of 12.5 joules per second.

(g) See figure 5.13.

(h) As the temperature increases the rate at which the rate of loss of heat increases is greater.

Note: The excess temperature is not directly proportional to the rate of loss of heat; if it was, you would have a straight line graph.

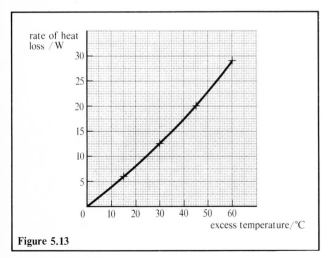

Figure 5.13

5.3 (a) Heat flows out as fast as it flows in: a steady state has been reached.

(b) In figure 5.2b (lagged bar), the temperature drops uniformly along the bar. No heat is lost from the sides, and the lines of heat flow are parallel.

In figure 5.2c (unlagged bar), the temperature drops more rapidly with distance near the hot end of the bar. Heat is lost from the sides. The rate of flow of heat through successive cross-sections decreases with distance, and the lines of heat flow are divergent.

(c) The temperature gradient is the slope of the graph. It is negative, because θ decreases as x increases. (i) The temperature gradient is constant, and is equal to $(\theta_2 - \theta_1)/x_1$, where x_1 is the distance between the places where θ_2 and θ_1 are measured. (ii) The temperature gradient is the slope of the curve at P and is equal to $d\theta/dx$ (it will decrease as the distance x along the bar increases).

(d) Rate of flow of heat is proportional to temperature gradient.

(e) Rate of flow of heat is proportional to cross-sectional area.

5.4 (a) Thermal conductivity is the quantity of heat which flows in 1 second through a cross-sectional area of 1 m² if the temperature gradient is 1 K m⁻¹.

(b) $\lambda = \left(\dfrac{dQ}{dt}\right)\left(\dfrac{1}{A}\right)\left(\dfrac{dx}{d\theta}\right)$

$\left[\text{unit of } \lambda\right] = \left[\dfrac{J}{s}\right]\left[\dfrac{1}{m^2}\right]\left[\dfrac{m}{K}\right]$

$[\text{unit of } \lambda] = [W\ m^{-1}\ K^{-1}]$

5.5 0.75 W m⁻¹ K⁻¹.

$15 \times 10^3\ W\ m^{-2} = \lambda \times \dfrac{100\ K}{5 \times 10^{-3}\ m}$.

5.6 (a) 1.8×10^4 W.

$\dfrac{Q}{t} = 0.8\ W\ m^{-1}\ K^{-1} \times 5\ m^2 \times \dfrac{18\ K}{4 \times 10^{-3}\ m}$.

(b) 6 electric fires.

(c) It has been assumed that the surface temperatures of the glass are the same as those of the surrounding air. In fact, this is not the case. Both sides of the glass are in contact with a layer of stationary air. There will be a temperature gradient across this layer and, consequently, the rate of transfer of heat will be considerably less. Also, the temperature of the room will not be uniform, because of convection currents.

(d) The heat loss can be reduced by double glazing and heavy curtains.

5.7 (a) 11.5 K.

The energy per second required to produce the steam is equal to the rate of flow of heat through the boiler plates. If θ is the temperature difference,

$\dfrac{(0.32\ kg)\,(2.3 \times 10^6\ J\ kg^{-1})}{1\ s} = \dfrac{48\ W\ m^{-1}\ K^{-1} \times 8\ m^2 \times}{6 \times 10^{-3}\ m}$

(b) There will be a layer of gas between the flame and the boiler plate which will reduce the rate of flow of heat. Also, if the water causes deposits of scale on the plate, there is a further reduction. The temperature difference between the flame and the water must therefore be higher than that calculated for the plates to maintain the rate of flow of heat required.

5.8 A deposit of scale around the element will cause the temperature of the element to increase, so that the temperature gradient across the scale allows a rate of transfer of heat equal to the rate at which electrical energy is being supplied. As the temperature of the element increases, the resistance of the element increases. The power available (V^2/R) decreases, so the water takes longer to boil. A deposit of scale on the inside walls has little effect, though it may reduce the rate of heat loss to the surroundings slightly.

5.9 3745 s.

Let x be the thickness of ice at a time t. Consider a surface area A. The lower surface of the ice must be at 0 °C (the freezing point of water), and the top surface is at a temperature θ. Temperature gradient $= \theta/x$,

rate of flow of heat through the ice $= \dfrac{\lambda_{ice} A \theta}{x}$.

Suppose that the thickness of the ice increases by δx in time δt, then

mass of ice formed $= \rho A \delta x$

energy supplied in a time $\delta t = l \rho A \delta x$

$$\lambda_{ice} A \frac{\theta}{x} = l \rho A \frac{\delta x}{\delta t}$$

Rearranging and integrating, we have

$$\int_0^t dt = \frac{l \rho A}{\lambda_{ice} \theta} \int_{x_2}^{x_1} x \, dx$$

$$[t]_0^t = \frac{l \rho A}{\lambda_{ice} \theta} \left[\frac{x^2}{2} \right]_{2 \times 10^{-2}}^{3 \times 10^{-2}}$$

Assume that the top surface of the ice is at the temperature of the air.

5.10 (a) 219 W.

Use the relation for flow of heat through co-axial cylinders of radii r_1 and r_2 and length l:

$$\frac{Q}{t} = \lambda \frac{2 \pi l \, (\theta_1 - \theta_2)}{\ln (r_2/r_1)}$$

(b) 9.7×10^{-5} kg s^{-1}.

5.12

Heat conduction		Electrical conduction	
rate of flow of heat	$\dfrac{Q}{t}$	rate of flow of charge	I
temperature gradient	$\dfrac{(\theta_1 - \theta_2)}{x}$	potential gradient	$\dfrac{V}{l}$
thermal conductivity	λ	electrical conductivity	σ

5.14 (a) A long bar.
(b) A thin disc with large cross-sectional area.
(c) A measurable flow of heat would not be obtained.
(d) A large surface area ensures that the rate of flow of heat is sufficiently large to measure.

5.16 (a) 4.0×10^2 W m^{-1} K^{-1}.

$$50 \text{ W} = \lambda \left(\pi \times \frac{25 \times 10^{-4} \text{ m}^2}{4} \right) \left(\frac{16 \text{ K}}{25 \times 10^{-2} \text{ m}} \right)$$

(b) (i) Diameter 0.2% (% error in area is 0.4%);
(ii) distance 0.2%;
(iii) difference in temperature 1.3%, $100 \times (2 \times 0.1)/16$;
(iv) rate of supply of heat 0.9%, $100 \times (0.02/5 + 0.05/5)$.
(c) 2.8% error.
(d) The measurement of temperature difference. Use thermoelectric thermometers to measure the temperatures.

5.18 For steady state conditions, the rate of heat flow through rock is equal to the rate of heat flow through silica. Assuming a negligible temperature drop across the copper,

$$\lambda_r A \frac{(\theta_1 - \theta_2)}{x_r} = \lambda_s A \frac{(\theta_2 - \theta_3)}{x_s}$$

$$\lambda_r = \lambda_s \left(\frac{x_r}{x_s} \right) \frac{(\theta_2 - \theta_3)}{(\theta_1 - \theta_2)}$$

5.19 0.17 W m^{-1} K^{-1}.

Power supplied $= 0.1$ A $\times 39$ V.
Since the electrical heater is arranged between the discs of material, only half the electrical energy that is transformed passes through each section.
For steady state conditions, assuming parallel flow,

$$\frac{3.9}{2} \text{W} = \lambda \frac{(4.13 \times 10^{-2} \text{ m}^2) (6.8 \text{ K})}{25 \times 10^{-3} \text{ m}}$$

5.20 (a) 293 K, or 20 °C.
(b) Plaster 80 K m^{-1}, brick 64 K m^{-1}.
(c) 48 W m^{-2}.
Consider a cross-sectional area A. For steady state conditions, if T is the temperature of the junction,

$$0.6 \text{ W m}^{-1} \text{ K}^{-1} \times A \times \frac{(295 \text{ K} - T)}{2.5 \times 10^{-2} \text{ m}}$$

$$= 0.75 \text{ W m}^{-1} \text{ K}^{-1} \times A \times \frac{(T - 277 \text{ K})}{25 \times 10^{-2} \text{ m}}$$

5.21 $R = x/\lambda$, so

$$[\text{ unit of } R] = \frac{[\text{ m }]}{[\text{ W m}^{-1} \text{K}^{-1}]} = [\text{ W}^{-1} \text{ m}^2 \text{ K }]$$

5.22 Brick wall:

$$\text{thermal resistance} = \frac{200 \times 10^{-3} \text{ m}}{0.8 \text{ W m}^{-1} \text{ K}^{-1}}$$

$$= 0.25 \text{ W}^{-1} \text{ m}^2 \text{ K}.$$

$$\Phi = \frac{20 \text{ K}}{0.25 \text{ W}^{-1} \text{ m}^2 \text{ K}} = 80 \text{ W m}^{-2}.$$

Cavity wall:

$$\text{thermal resistance} = \left(\frac{200 \times 10^{-3}}{0.8} + \frac{50 \times 10^{-3}}{0.03} \right) \frac{\text{m}}{\text{W m}^{-1} \text{K}^{-1}}$$

$$= 1.92 \text{ W}^{-1} \text{ m}^2 \text{ K}.$$

$$\Phi = \frac{20 \text{ K}}{1.92 \text{ W}^{-1} \text{ m}^2 \text{ K}} = 10 \text{ W m}^{-2}.$$

5.23 Rate of flow of heat per unit area is reduced.
Total thermal resistance $= (0.1 + 0.05 + 0.25)$ W^{-1} m^2 K
$$= 0.4 \text{ W}^{-1} \text{ m}^2 \text{ K.}$$

$$\Phi = \frac{20 \text{ K}}{0.4 \text{ W}^{-1} \text{ m}^2 \text{ K}} = 50 \text{ W m}^{-2}.$$

5.24 (a) From $\dfrac{Q}{t} = \lambda A \dfrac{(\theta_1 - \theta_2)}{x}$

thermal transmittance $= \dfrac{Q}{t\, A\, (\theta_1 - \theta_2)} = \dfrac{\lambda}{x}$

The unit of thermal transmittance is W m^{-2} K^{-1}.

(b) $U = \dfrac{1}{R}$.

5.25 (a)

Thermal resistance of component	R/W^{-1} m^2 K
R_{so}	0.05
R_{brick}	0.12
R_{cav}	0.18
$R_{concrete}$	0.43
$R_{plaster}$	0.06
R_{si}	0.12
total =	0.96

$$U = \frac{1}{0.96 \text{ W}^{-1} \text{ m}^2 \text{ K}} = 1.04 \text{ W m}^{-2} \text{ K}^{-1}$$

(b) Deduct R_{cav} from the thermal resistance of the original construction and add R_{foam}.
Total thermal resistance $= (0.96 - 0.18 + 1.67)$ W^{-1} m^2 K
$$= 2.45 \text{ W}^{-1} \text{ m}^2 \text{ K.}$$

$$U = \frac{1}{2.45 \text{ W}^{-1} \text{ m}^2 \text{ K}} = 0.41 \text{ W m}^{-2} \text{ K}^{-1}$$

(c) Rate of loss of heat for unfilled cavity = 168 W,
rate of loss of heat for filled cavity = 66 W.

5.26 Sound energy. The vibrations of the crystal lattice are often regarded as resembling the passage of elastic waves (or acoustic waves) of very high frequency (typically 10^{13} Hz) through the material.

5.27 Free electrons.

Chapter 6
6.2 Because thermal equilibrium is reached when the rate at which the exposed surface is receiving energy is equal to the rate at which energy is being transferred to the surroundings.

6.5 A dull black surface absorbs more radiation than a highly polished white surface. This can be demonstrated by an experiment using a Leslie cube. (If you are not familiar with this experiment, refer to an O level physics text book.)

6.6 (a) A will absorb most of the radiation that falls on it. To prevent its temperature rising above that of the surroundings (a situation which is contrary to experience) it will radiate equally to the surroundings. It is therefore a good emitter.
(b) B will reflect most of the radiation to the surroundings, consequently it will only radiate back to the surroundings an amount equal to the small amount absorbed. It is therefore a poor emitter.
(c) C will strongly emit radiation in this particular waveband so that its temperature does not rise above that of the surroundings. Thus, each body in the enclosure radiates exactly as much energy to the enclosure as it receives from it.

6.7 For thermal equilibrium, D is absorbing radiation at the same rate at which it is emitting radiation. Since it is a black body, it is emitting black body radiation. Consequently it must also be receiving black body radiation.

6.9 If $\Phi = AT^n$, then $\lg \Phi = n \lg T + \lg A$.
A graph of $\lg (\Phi/\text{W})$ against $\lg (T/\text{K})$ gives a straight line, as in figure 6.13.
(b) n is 3.8 ± 0.2. It is obtained by calculating the gradient (slope) of the graph.
(c) A is about 10^{-11} W K^{-4}. $\dfrac{\lg A}{2.75} = -\dfrac{0.6}{0.15}$

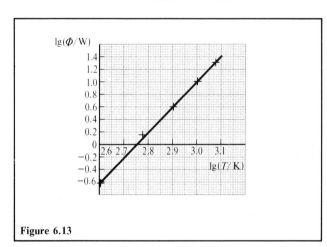

Figure 6.13

6.10 (a) $A\sigma T^4$.

(b) $B\sigma T_0^4$.

(c) All the radiation emitted by P strikes the outer sphere, but only a proportion of the radiation from Q is absorbed by P. (If you consider a point on the inner surface of sphere Q, only radiation within the angle θ is intercepted by the sphere P.)

(d) (i) $A\sigma T_0^4$ (ii) It must be the same as the power radiated.

(e) The area factor for the radiation from the outer sphere to the inner sphere must also be equal to A.

$\Phi_{\text{loss}} = A\sigma T^4$, and $\Phi_{\text{gain}} = A\sigma T_0^4$

thus $\Phi_{\text{net}} = A\sigma T^4 - A\sigma T_0^4$

$\qquad = A\sigma(T^4 - T_0^4)$

6.11 62.4 W.

Using $\Phi_{\text{net}} = \sigma A (T^4 - T_0^4)$

$\Phi_{\text{net}} = [\,5.7 \times 10^{-8}\ \text{W m}^{-2}\,\text{K}^{-4}\,]\,[\,4\,\pi \times (4 \times 10^{-2}\ \text{m})^2\,] \times$
$\qquad\qquad\qquad\qquad\qquad\qquad [(500\ \text{K})^4 - (300\ \text{K})^4]$

6.13 (a) 390 W.

$\Phi_{\text{net}} = 5.7 \times 10^{-8} \times 2 \times (320^4 - 290^4)$ W.

(b) Heat is also transferred to the surroundings by convection, and there will be some conduction through the supporting brackets.

6.14 430 W.

$\Phi_{\text{net}} = 0.6 \times 5.7 \times 10^{-8} \times 2 \times (340^4 - 290^4)$ W.

6.15 3390 K.

$150\ \text{W} = 0.4\ (5.7 \times 10^{-8}\ \text{W m}^{-2}\,\text{K}^{-4})\ (50 \times 10^{-6}\ \text{m}^2)\ T^4$

where T is the temperature of the filament.

Assume that $T \gg$ temperature of surroundings.

6.16 (a) Surface area of filament, $A = 2\,\pi\,r\,l$

power radiated, $\Phi = \sigma A\ T^4$

therefore, $\Phi = \sigma 2\,\pi\,r\,l\ T^4$

(b) Resistance of filament $R = \dfrac{\rho l}{\pi\,r^2}$

where ρ is the resistivity.

Electrical power supplied $P = V^2/R$

$$P = \frac{V^2\,\pi\,r^2}{\rho l}$$

(c) For steady conditions $\Phi = P$, so

$$\sigma 2\,\pi\,r\,l\,T^4 = \frac{V^2\,\pi\,r^2}{\rho l}$$

$T^4 \propto r/l^2$

6.17 Radius 58 μm, length 36 mm.

$60\ \text{W} = (5.7 \times 10^{-8}\ \text{W m}^{-2}\,\text{K}^{-4})\ 2\pi rl\ (3000\ \text{K})^4$ $\qquad$ (1)

$60\ \text{W} = \dfrac{(12\ \text{V})^2\,\pi\,r^2}{(7.0 \times 10^{-7}\,\Omega\,\text{m})\,l}$

Substituting for l in equation (1) and rearranging,

$r^3 = \dfrac{60^2 \times 7.0 \times 10^{-7}}{12^2 \times 5.7 \times 10^{-8} \times 2\pi^2 \times 3000^4}$ m^3

$r = 5.8 \times 10^{-5}$ m.

Substitute for r in equation (1) to find l.

6.18 1.6×10^3 W m^{-2}.

Let S be the power received per unit area.

Total power radiated by sun $= 4\,\pi\,R^2\,S$.

Power radiated per unit area is given by

$\dfrac{\Phi}{A} = \dfrac{4\,\pi\,R^2\,S}{4\,\pi\,r^2}$

From Stefan's law

$\dfrac{\Phi_{\text{net}}}{A} = \sigma(T^4 - T_0^4)$

where T and T_0 are the temperatures of sun and earth respectively. (T_0^4 is small compared to T^4 and can be neglected.)

Thus $\sigma T^4 = \dfrac{R^2\,S}{r^2}$

$S = \dfrac{\sigma T^4\,r^2}{R^2}$

$S = \dfrac{(5.7 \times 10^{-8}\ \text{W m}^{-2}\,\text{K}^{-4})\,(6000\ \text{K})^4\,(7.0 \times 10^8\ \text{m})2}{(1.5 \times 10^{11}\ \text{m})^2}$

$S = 1.6 \times 10^3$ W m^{-2}.

6.19 1.75×10^5 s (48.6 hours).

Assume that the loss of heat from the hot water is negligible, or included in the efficiency of the system.

Energy required to increase temperature
$\qquad = (5\text{m}^3)\,(1 \times 10^3\ \text{kg m}^{-3})\,(4.2 \times 10^3\ \text{J kg}^{-1}\,\text{K}^{-1})\,(60\text{K})$
$\qquad = 1.26 \times 10^9$ J

Power absorbed by solar panel $= (600\ \text{W m}^{-2})\,(20\ \text{m}^2)$

Energy transferred $= \dfrac{60}{100}\,(1.2 \times 10^4\ \text{W})\,t$

where t is the time required.

$1.26 \times 10^9\ \text{J} = \dfrac{60}{100}\,(1.2 \times 10^4\ \text{W})\,t$

$t = 1.75 \times 10^5$ s.

6.21 (a) As the wavelength increases the power radiated per unit area in each narrow waveband, $M_{\lambda,\mathrm{B}}$, increases to a maximum value and then decreases. (The maximum value depends upon the temperature of the black body.)

(b) (i) The power radiated per unit area between λ_1 and $\lambda_1 + \delta\lambda$. (ii) W m^{-2}.

(c) The total area under the curve represents the total power radiated per unit area (total radiant exitance M_B) of the black body at the particular temperature.
The sum of all the values of $M_{\lambda,\mathrm{B}}\,\delta\lambda$ can be expressed as

$$M_\mathrm{B} = \int_0^\infty M_{\lambda,\mathrm{B}}\, d\lambda$$

(d) It is proportional to the fourth power of the thermodynamic temperature (Stefan's law).

(e) The slit width of the detecting instrument.
Note: The slit does not receive the same range of wavelengths in different parts of the spectrum. The dispersion of the prism is a function of wavelength: a correction is made for this.

6.24 As the temperature of the body increases, the wavelength at which the intensity is maximum decreases. Since $\lambda_\mathrm{r} > \lambda_\mathrm{y}$, the colour changes from red to yellow as the temperature of the body increases.
Note: Between about 500 °C and 1500 °C the temperature of a body can be estimated from its colour.

6.25 5918 K. (The temperature of the radiating surface of the sun is about 6000 K.)
Applying Wien's displacement law,
$(4.9 \times 10^{-7}\,\mathrm{m})\,T = 2.9 \times 10^{-3}\,\mathrm{m\ K}$.

6.27 (a) The non-black body curve has a similar shape to the black body curve: M_λ increases to a maximum and then decreases with increasing wavelength. The maximum value of M_λ is at the same wavelength as the maximum value of $M_{\lambda,\mathrm{B}}$. (For this body the ratio of $M_\lambda/M_{\lambda,\mathrm{B}}$ for each waveband is about the same.)

(b) (i) The area underneath the non-black body curve,

$$M = \int_0^\infty M_\lambda\, d\lambda$$

(ii) It is the ratio of the area underneath the non-black body curve to the area underneath the black body curve.

(c) $\epsilon = M/M_\mathrm{B}$.

(d) This follows from Prévost's theory. For thermal equilibrium, the power radiated is equal to the total power absorbed.

(e) The total power radiated per unit area by the non-black body is ϵM_B.
The non-black body is in a uniform temperature enclosure. It receives black body radiation. The fraction absorbed per unit area of surface is αM_B.
Hence $\epsilon M_\mathrm{B} = \alpha M_\mathrm{B}$
$\epsilon = \alpha$

6.28 (a) The total emissivity and the total absorptance of a surface range from 0 for a perfect reflector to 1 for a black body.

6.29 (a) This non-black body curve does not follow the black body curve. The ratio of $M_\lambda/M_{\lambda,\mathrm{B}}$ for each waveband of width $\delta\lambda$ varies.

(b) The power radiated per unit area by the non-black body in the waveband λ_1 to $\lambda_1 + \delta\lambda$.

(c) The power radiated per unit area by the black body in the waveband λ_1 to $\lambda_1 + \delta\lambda$.

6.30 By similar reasoning to 6.27 (e), but considering radiation in a narrow waveband $\delta\lambda$, it follows that $\epsilon_\lambda = \alpha_\lambda$ for a specified waveband and temperature.

Appendixes

A1 The area of all the strips represents the total number of cars passing in the fixed interval with speeds between 60 m s^{-1} and 70 m s^{-1}. Figure A3 gives this number as 64 cars, which agrees with figure A2.

A2 The unit of N_c is s m^{-1}. The shaded area represents the number of molecules with speeds between 200 m s^{-1} and 202 m s^{-1}. The area represents a number, without a unit.

A3 Using $pV_\mathrm{m} = RT$,

$$R = \frac{(1.013 \times 10^5\,\mathrm{Pa})\,(22.4 \times 10^{-3}\,\mathrm{m^3\ mol^{-1}})}{273.15\ \mathrm{K}}$$

$$= 8.31\ \mathrm{J\ mol^{-1}\ K^{-1}}.$$

A4 Relative molecular mass of $CO_2 = 44$,
molar mass of CO_2, $M_\mathrm{m} = 44 \times 10^{-3}\,\mathrm{kg\ mol^{-1}}$.
Thus 44×10^{-3} kg of CO_2 will occupy 22.4×10^{-3} m^3,
2.2×10^{-3} kg of CO_2 will occupy 1.12×10^{-3} m^3.

Standard symbols used in this Unit

Symbol	Quantity	Unit	Symbol for unit
α_λ	absorptance, spectral		
λ	absorptance, total		
n	amount of substance	mole	mol
A	area, cross-section	metre squared	m^2
A	area, surface	metre squared	m^2
I	current	ampere	A
ρ	density	kilogram per metre cubed	$kg\ m^{-3}$
σ	electrical conductivity	siemens per metre	$S\ m^{-1}$
ϵ_λ	emissivity, spectral		
ϵ	emissivity, total	dimensionless	
E	energy	joule	J
α	expansivity, linear	per kelvin	K^{-1}
F	force	newton	N
C	heat capacity	joule per kelvin	$J\ K^{-1}$
U	internal energy	joule	J
L	latent heat	joule	J
l, x	length	metre	m
m	mass	kilogram	kg
λ	mean free path	metre	m
$\bar{c}$	mean molecular speed	metre per second	$m\ s^{-1}$
R	molar gas constant	joule per mole kelvin	$J\ mol^{-1}\ K^{-1}$
C_p	molar heat capacity at constant pressure	joule per mole kelvin	$J\ mol^{-1}\ K^{-1}$
C_V	molar heat capacity at constant volume	joule per mole kelvin	$J\ mol^{-1}\ K^{-1}$
M_m	molar mass	kilogram per mole	$kg\ mol^{-1}$
σ	molecular diameter	metre	m
N	number of molecules of gas		

Symbol	Quantity	Unit	Symbol for unit
V	potential difference	volt	V
P	power	watt	W
p	pressure	pascal	Pa
Q	quantity of heat	joule	J
r	radius	metre	m
M_λ	radiant exitance, spectral	watt per metre cubed	$W\ m^{-3}$
M	radiant exitance, total	watt per metre squared	$W\ m^{-2}$
Φ	radiant power	watt	W
γ	ratio C_p/C_V	dimensionless	
ρ	resistivity	ohm metre	$\Omega\ m$
$c_{r.m.s.}, \sqrt{\overline{c^2}}$	root mean square speed	metre per second	$m\ s^{-1}$
c	specific heat capacity	joule per kilogram kelvin	$J\ kg^{-1}\ K^{-1}$
l	specific latent heat	joule per kilogram	$J\ kg^{-1}$
γ	surface tension	newton per metre	$N\ m^{-1}$
θ	temperature, common (Celsius)	degree Celsius	°C
T	temperature, thermodynamic (absolute)	kelvin	K
T_c	temperature, critical	kelvin	K
T_{tr}	temperature, triple point	kelvin	K
λ	thermal conductivity	watt per metre kelvin	$W\ m^{-1}\ K^{-1}$
V	volume	metre cubed	m^3
λ	wavelength	metre	m
W	work	joule	J

Abbreviations used in the text

Adkins   Adkins, C.H. *Thermal physics*. Hodder & Stoughton, 1976.

Bolton   Bolton, W. *Patterns in physics*. McGraw Hill, 1974.

Duncan MM   Duncan, T. *Advanced physics: materials and mechanics*. John Murray, 1973.

Duncan FWA   Duncan, T. *Advanced physics; fields, waves and atoms*. John Murray, 1975.

Hands   Hands, R.A. *Heat for advanced courses*. G. Bell, 1974.

Millar   Akrill, T.B., Bennet, G.A.G. and Millar, C.J. *Physics*. Edward Arnold, 1979.

Nelkon   Nelkon, M. and Parker, P. *Advanced level physics*. Heinemann, 4th edition (SI), 1977.

Thorning   Thorning, W.E. *The gaseous phase*. John Murray, 1974.

Wenham   Wenham, E.J., Dorling, G.W., Snell, J.A.N. and Taylor, B. *Physics: concepts and models*. Addison Wesley, 1972.

Whelan   Whelan, P.M. and Hodgson, M.J. *Essential principles of physics*. John Murray, 1978.

Values of physical constants

Quantity	Symbol	Value	Unit
Boltzmann constant	k	1.38×10^{-23}	$J\ K^{-1}$
Avogadro constant	N_A	6.0×10^{23}	mol^{-1}
molar gas constant	R	8.3	$J\ mol^{-1}\ K^{-1}$
Stefan-Boltzmann constant	σ	5.7×10^{-8}	$W\ m^{-2}\ K^{-4}$
triple point of water	T_{tr}	273.16	K
absolute zero		0	K
ice point		273.15	K
steam point		373.15	K
standard pressure		1.013×10^5	Pa
standard temperature		273.15	K

Acknowledgments

Thanks are due to the following, who have kindly permitted the reproduction of copyright photographs: Cover, Barnaby's Picture Library; page 4, British Steel Corporation; page 24, The Science Museum, London; page 40, Photo CERN and the Royal Society; page 54, Banton and Co., Ltd.; page 66, Daily Telegraph Colour Library; page 72, P.G. Tucker; page 74, British Gas Corporation.

Question 3 on page 13 is reproduced by permission of the University of London Examinations Council, and question 5 on page 13 by permission of the Oxford Schools Examination Board. Question 5.2 on page 56 is reproduced by permission of the Oxford and Cambridge Schools Examination Board/Nuffield O level physics. The 'Comprehension exercise' questions 1-7 on page 38 and questions 1-8 on pages 76-7 are reproduced by permission of the Joint Matriculation Board.

The article on pages 37-8 is adapted from *The stars: their structure and evolution* by R.J. Tayler, Vol. 10 of Wykeham Science Series. The article on pages 76-7 is adapted from 'Medical Thermography', *Scientific American,* February 1967.

Project team   John Bausor (Director)
                      Leslie Beckett
                      Allan Covell
                      David Davies
                      Martin Hollins

Printed in Great Britain by Martin's of Berwick

0 7195 3604 9 (Student's guide)
0 7195 3605 7 (Teacher's guide)